The Vermont Heritage Songbook

By Margaret MacArthur
with Gregory Sharrow

The Vermont Folklife Center
Middlebury, Vermont

Library of Congress Cataloging-in-Publication Data

MacArthur, Magaret, 1928-
  The Vermont heritage songbook / by Margaret MacArthur with Gregory
Sharrow.
    p. of music.
    Melodies with chord symbols.
    Lyrics by Vermont schoolchildren, set by MacArthur to original and traditional
  tunes.
    Includes notes on Vermont history, folklore, and social life and customs of the
  past, which formed the inspiration for the songs.
    ISBN 0-916718-13-1

    1. Songs. English—Vermont. 2. Vermont—Songs and music.
  I. Sharrow, Gregory. II. Title.
  M1629.7.V5M33   1994
                                                          94-34884
                                                             CIP
                                                              M

The Vermont Folklife Center
The Gamaliel Painter House
P.O. Box 442
Middlebury, Vermont 05753

Dedicated
to the
memory of
Patrick MacArthur.

Table of Contents

Looking Back on the 20th Century

Acknowledgements

Our thanks, first of all, to the Lamson Howell Foundation, the Vermont Community Foundation, the Vermont Historical Society, and the Wells River Savings Bank for major contributions toward the production costs of this publication. Our thanks also to the Bradford Historical Society, the Brattleboro Savings and Loan, the Marlboro Community Club, the Marlboro Historical Society, the Northfield Savings Bank, Stanley Tools Eagle Square Plant, the Vermont National Bank, the Weathersfield Historical Society, the Williston Historical Society, and the Williston PTA for their financial contributions to the project.

Special thanks to Arts Coordinators Kathy Link of Shaftsbury, Anne Taylor of Orange East, and Judy Simon-Boughton of Ascutney for working closely with Margaret MacArthur in their districts. Thanks also to the students and teachers who researched and wrote the verses of these songs: Bill Colvin and his 6th grade and Fran Andres and her 6th grade at the Shaftsbury School (June 1987), Grade 8 at the Miller Run School in Sheffield (1987), Shayne Lylis and her 4th grade at the Sherburne School (December 1987), Kathy Holmes and her 5th/6th grade at the Peacham School (October 1988), Linda Bourne and her 6th grade at the Guilford School (November 1988), Patrice Miller and her 6th grade at the Derby School (January 1989), Grade 5/6 at the West Haven School (January 1989), Linda Heaton and her 1st grade and Suzanne Dirmaier and her 5th grade at the Warren School (September 1989), Grace Freeman and her 3rd/4th grade and Pat Koledo and her 3rd/4th grade at the Brewster Pierce School in Huntington (October 1990), Richard Allen and a multi-age team at the Williston School (November 1990), Teri Ober and her 5th grade, Susan Kreps and her 5th grade, and Christine Cook and her 5th grade at the Georgia School (October 1991), Marilyn Bish and her 5th grade and Linda Peoro and her 5th grade at the Swanton School (March 1991), Grade 5/6 team at the Randolph Village School (March 1991), Gary Lamoureaux and his 4th grade at the Pownal school (March 1991), Helen Freismuth and her 5th/6th grade at the Weybridge School (April 1991), Grade 5 at the Fairlee School (April 1991), Sara Barrett and her 2nd grade, Margaret Morse and her 2nd/3rd grade and Cindy Lyon and her 5th/6th grade at the Duxbury School (1991), John Esau and his Junior Room students and David Holtzapfel and his Senior Room students at the Marlboro School (May 1991), Judy Locke and her 5th grade at the Craftsbury School (June 1991), Karen McGee and her 2nd grade at the Perkinsville School (1992), Glenda Rose and her 3rd grade at the Bradford School (April 1993), and Trudy Fadden and Mary Hays and their 4th/5th grade at the Newbury School (October 1993).

These students and their dedicated teachers devoted enormous amounts of time and energy to this project. Without them it could never have happened — this truly is their book. Proceeds generated from the sale of this book will support future Vermont Folklife Center educational outreach programs to enrich the classroom experience of Vermont school children like these.

Thanks also to the Vermont Folklife Center's Teacher Advisory Group and to readers Kaye Alexander, John MacArthur, Jessica Sharrow, Alice Leeds, and Meg Ostrum. As always Folklife Center staff members — Jane Beck, Meg Ostrum, Susan O'Brien, and Terri Jackman — have offered important support for various stages of the production process. Special thanks to Jerry Rockwell and Mary Lautzenheiser for helping Margaret cope with the headaches of learning a new computer program for music. Copy editor Susan Littlefield, musicians Ruth Wright and Edith Thomas, and music proofreader John Roberts have provided an indispensable service ensuring accuracy and consistency in the text and music. As music engraver, John Roberts has also created clear, consistent musical notation for all 42 songs, a monumental undertaking which we deeply appreciate. Lisa Preston has provided guitar chords for each song, enhancing this book's usefulness. Graphic designer Tina Christensen and illustrator Bonnie Christensen have done a masterful of job bringing all of the pieces into a coherent and pleasing whole. And Kaye Alexander's vision has guided the entire process as we've worked together toward a finished book.

Finally and most importantly, our thanks to our families for seeing us through the ups-and-downs of a project which has spanned a number of years. It is a great pleasure to acknowledge their ongoing love and support.

Foreword

History is most compelling when it tells us about people and the lives they led. But for generations, published histories focused only on great men and the political, economic, and military events which defined each era. Much important information was missing. What was everyday life like in frontier Vermont? What went on in rural Vermont communities during the last century? What was most memorable about growing up on a Vermont farm in the early 1900s? We need answers to these questions in order to understand how the past has shaped our present and to plan for the best of all possible futures.

When folklorists study the past they are especially interested in all of the details about how people lived — their folklife or traditional culture. This information is common knowledge to the people who've lived it, but it's quick to vanish as the generations pass on. The Vermont Folklife Center is a non-profit organization dedicated to supporting and preserving this important cultural heritage. Through interviews with senior Vermonters as well as archival research, we piece together a picture of life in the past to share with you, through exhibits, audio and video recordings, publications, workshops, and college-level classes. The Folklife Center's Peabody Award-winning public radio series "Journey's End: The Memories and Traditions of Daisy Turner and Her Family" and our popular teaching resource *Many Cultures, One People: A Multicultural Handbook about Vermont for Teachers* are but two examples of ways we bring Vermont's rich heritage to a broad audience statewide.

This songbook is an unusual project. It represents the collaborative work of Margaret MacArthur with school children and their teachers in towns throughout the state. Margaret is a singer-scholar who has researched the traditional music of New England and performed from this repertoire for audiences around the country. Under the auspices of the Vermont Council on the Arts, she has also been an artist-in-residence in many Vermont schools. In 1987 she undertook a new kind of residency project at the Shaftsbury School, inspired by Arts and Basics Program director Kathy Link. Working closely with Kathy, Margaret helped students use information from interviews with older residents to compose a series of songs about their town. She later repeated this process in schools around the state. As Margaret explains,

"We engaged in communal creation, with every member of the group participating in one aspect or another, from the initial planning to the final performance. Our most important step was tracking down and choosing a good story, one that would interest students, teachers, townsfolk, and me. Information came from oral history interviews or local histories. Once we were familiar with the story, we took down all of the ideas that flowed from the students, made lists of rhyming words, and then made verses. At this point a tune usually came to me, either a traditional one or a new composition fitted to our creation. Everyone made some contribution as the poem was edited for clarity and each line honed to fit the tune. In a series of ten classroom sessions we could make a fine song. All of our final performances for the school or the town were extremely successful, the songs being sung from memory with gusto and pride. The unflagging interest, help, and encouragement of the school staff were essential to our intense bursts of creation in such short periods of time."

Helen Freismuth teaches fifth and sixth grades in Weybridge. She offers a teacher's perspective on Margaret's residency and the song-writing process:

"We began by reading the town history written by the local historical society. After gaining some awareness of the town's settlement and development, we began interviewing town elders. Talking with townspeople and hearing their stories brought an urgency and ownership to the students' learning. People told these stories to the students with sincerity; the students listened with respect and sensitivity. They knew that important information and feelings were being shared. Writing the lyrics was an astounding process of collaboration and cooperation. Margaret met with groups of six students and helped each group find the essence of these stories, the common threads of history and the common threads of human life. She worked with each group to organize the pieces of stories in a meaningful way, in every case maintaining the integrity of the elders' own stories and words, and the student authors' sense of style and voice. Students' investment in the songs grew as

Margaret set the lyrics to music. The music was authentic and the words were true. Sung as ballads the poems carried the students to an earlier time. The history of the town and the history of the people became a personal history for each student."

Margaret MacArthur's song-writing residencies spanned a number of years, with the majority taking place during Vermont's bicentennial celebration in 1990-91. Several residencies were jointly supported by the Vermont Council on the Arts and the Vermont Folklife Center as a special bicentennial project. These residencies resulted in a collection of over 80 songs. Margaret was impressed with their artistic and historical merit and was determined that they should reach a broader audience. The Vermont Folklife Center was pleased to become a partner in creating this publication.

Nearly half of the songs from Margaret's residencies are presented here, with at least one song from each participating school. Margaret has made small changes in the lyrics and shortened several of the songs, but the songs remain a collaborative creation between artist and students. She has also included five Vermont songs from other sources, songs which are her favorites and are frequently requested when she performs. As an added teaching tool, the Vermont Folklife Center's Director of Education, Dr. Gregory Sharrow, has written a series of brief historical essays to accompany each song. Greg has also grouped songs

chronologically and has indexed each song for basic topics in Vermont history. Alice Leeds, a teacher at the Lincoln School who frequently uses music in her classroom, has contributed an introduction with suggestions for integrating music into the regular curriculum.

This songbook represents a unique way of involving children with the history of our state. Each song is based on information that is the product of detailed local research. This information is specific to particular places but at the same time is universal. From the terror of catamounts and the times of starvation to old-time sugaring and the general store, these songs present the essence of Vermont experience down through the years. Pay close attention to the lyrics because every word counts. Farmers really did tar their turkeys' feet before the long drive to Boston and "swingling" and "hetcheling" are precise old-time terms for stages in the process of making linen. Likewise, Vermont folk speech from the children's interviews is present in the song texts. "Nooning" and "maudle" are real words that were a part of everyday speech of this region. This kind of material has been woven into every song. These are not just pretty lyrics — they're student research cast into verse.

It is with great pleasure that we at the Vermont Folklife Center offer this book to teachers and others who work with young people in Vermont, as well as history lovers of all ages. Our state has a rich cultural heritage and it is essential that our young people grow up understanding that it is their heritage as well. We think that this songbook is a wonderful resource. We're certain that you will too.

Introduction

My richest and most vivid experiences as an educator have been those in which children were immersed in creative pursuits — combining their learning with the exploration of poetry, music, artwork, dramatics, and movement. Music has additionally been a powerful force in establishing a creative environment and weaving together various art forms for presentation.

During a summer environmental education program in Bar Harbor, Maine, my pre-school participants traversed the foothills, streams, sand bars, and tidepools of Mount Desert Island while singing Gordon Bok's wonderful tunes about sea otters, sailors, and Isle au Haut. When I was a Montessori teacher in Durham, North Carolina, working with 6-9 years olds, my students discovered they could complete their work contracts by combining music with research. They would gather information about a particular topic and use our collection of classroom percussion instruments to accompany a song and movement presentation on such topics as Australian penguins or ancient crinoids. Later, in my 4th-6th grade classroom in the mountains of Lincoln, Vermont, small groups of students collaborated on musical accompaniment to their research-based poems on astronomy or their more passionate poems on rain, friendship, and flying.

My students are always eager to create plays, dances, visual presentations, and songs to display and develop their learning, regardless of whether the audience is their peers, their parents, or the school community. Music has been an effective component of student-created videos, slide shows, Hypercard stacks, and performances. And given the time and space, children have been willing to revise and fine-tune their work to produce a polished presentation worthy of any audience.

Through the years I have discovered — along with many colleagues — that children thrive on and benefit from the opportunity to apply their creativity in learning situations. Howard Gardner's theory of multiple intelligences and other researchers' work on learning styles, superlearning, and creative imagery have acknowledged and confirmed what many of us gleaned from our own personal experiences: music, movement, poetry, drama, and the fine arts not only add pleasure to the learning experience, but can also intensify it. It has been my observation that children who present a research topic using a spectrum of the arts are able to recall their knowledge again and again, always with renewed enthusiasm. The concepts are embedded in their memories through images, sound, rhythm, and movement, ready to spring back to life as the need arises.

This book provides a wonderful opportunity to link the arts with Vermont studies. The songs Margaret MacArthur and her students composed speak of general stores and chores, early settlers and native Vermonters, legends and logging, hermits and healing, steamboats and sugaring, daily life and extraordinary events. Gregory Sharrow, the Vermont Folklife Center's Director of Education, has provided contextual information for each song to place the story lines in a broader historical perspective. Whether you work with children in a classroom, a recreational setting, or in your own home, there are countless ways to use this collection. Some suggestions are listed here. While many of them are oriented to the classroom, others can be used by parents, day care providers, and counselors, one-on-one or in small groups. It doesn't really matter where you start. Creative pursuits, once begun, take on a life of their own. Don't be afraid to ask children to fine-tune some of their creative work; this is often the most rewarding part of their experience. As my primary students and I concluded while working on one of our integrated projects, "Art is serious work!" I might add, it is also serious play. Taking the arts seriously is a way to make work joyful and fun deeply rewarding.

Drama and Movement

Invite a group of five or six children to act out the story line of one of the songs in mime. If everyone in the group has learned the song, some children can sing while others improvise in mime. Small groups of children can choreograph a dance or mime presentation to accompany a song. The larger group might like to collaborate on a simple folk dance to go along with a song. Alternatively, small groups of children can create mini-plays about the story line in one of the songs and then share their plays with each other after everyone has become familiar with the songs.

Language Arts and Social Studies

As you learn each song, read and discuss the accompanying background information. Perhaps children can add to this with their own family stories. Summarize the key events in a song. Discuss the connection between the tone of the story and the mood set by its melodic line. Compare a favorite song to another similar song, poem, or story. Rewrite a song in another literary genre. Ask each child to prepare a retelling of one of the songs in the oral tradition.

Working With the Music Teacher

Teachers who are planning a culminating event for their Vermont unit may wish to enlist the support of the music teacher in preparing the class to present one of the songs. For added interest, teachers might offer to assist the music teacher by adding simple percussive accompaniment or working with the students to choreograph a contra dance, creative movement, or mime piece to accompany the song. Please note: alter the key of any song to accommodate student voices as needed.

Music and Art

Listen for the musical quality of each song. Is the mood happy (major key) or sad (minor key)? Does the tempo make you want to dance or sway, or just sit back and take it in? Do certain phrases ask to be sung more loudly or quietly, quickly or slowly? Contrast and compare the songs in this collection with each other in terms of their musical qualities. Why do certain songs have more appeal to you than others? Memorize the words and melody to one song, then share it at a community or family gathering or school assembly. (Put the chorus on chart paper so everyone can sing along.) Choose one appealing melody and write new lyrics or an additional verse.

Encourage children to use various small and large percussion instruments (bells, chimes, gongs, hand drums, finger cymbals, and wood blocks) when creating their poetry, mime or drama presentations.

Music is a powerful catalyst for fine art. Provide children with paper, pencils, and paint sets. Sing one of the songs they are familiar with, asking them to focus on images that the song brings to mind. Establish a calm mood in the room, then invite children to create paintings or poems inspired by the song.

Other Ideas

The previous suggestions can be approached without much additional planning on your part. If you are feeling energetic, you may wish to use this book as a springboard for an exciting local history project reaching beyond the boundaries of your school or organization. In this way, you will have the opportunity to experience the kind of primary source learning undertaken by Margaret and her students. Here are a few possibilities if you decide to go this adventurous route:

ORAL HISTORY: Research a local event, place, or tradition, or interview a group of town or family elders about life in their younger days. Your local historical society or church may be able to assist you in locating people. After gathering research, discuss which historic events might inspire a song. Write a poem, story, or song about one of these events. Make a presentation to your family, organization, school, or local historical society, or publish your collection of folklore.

MUSIC AND LOCAL MUSICIANS: Expose children to the music and fine or folk art of various cultures and time periods. Ask them to attempt to copy these forms or to translate them into our own time and culture. Gather books and recordings of traditional music and dance. (There is probably a musician in your family or among your students' parents who would love to assist you.) Research and learn to hear the distinction between a ballad and a lyric song, a waltz and a jig, or the difference between a tune in a major and a minor key. Research traditional songs, instruments, and dance. Seek out traditional musicians in your town to talk to or perform for the children. Invite your student musicians to practice and perform a traditional American tune for the group. (The music teacher may be willing to assist you.) Organize a community contra dance accompanied by local musicians. Encourage student musicians to sit in with the band on tunes they have learned.

ARTIST-IN-RESIDENCE: There is nothing like the presence of an artist to inspire children. That's how this book was created. The Vermont Council on the Arts has an extensive registry of artists who are experienced in working with children and available for residencies in communities throughout the state. If you apply by the end of the preceding June, the Council may be able to assist with funding your residency.

Whichever suggestions you use, I am certain you will find, as did the children who worked with Margaret MacArthur on these songs, that music is more than an isolated skill or talent. It can and should be part of the fabric of our daily lives, enriching our appreciation for the world around us and for the remarkable chain of people and events that have carried us to this time and place.

— Alice Leeds
Intermediate Multi-age Teacher,
Lincoln Community School (Lincoln, VT)
Curriculum Implementation Specialist,
Addison Northeast Supervisory Union (Bristol, VT)

Pioneer Vermont

People of the Dawn

Several members of the team of students in Marilyn Bish's Grade 5 in Swanton were of Abenaki heritage. Jeanne Brink came to school to tell this story that had been passed down in her family. The Abenaki verse, as well as the tune of this song, is from Jeanne's recording of the singing of her grandmother Elvine Obomsawin Royce.

Swanton

Have you ever heard the saying, "There are two sides to every story?" That's especially true when it comes to history, because the people who win the wars get to tell what happened. We learn about everything from the winner's point of view, and the other side's perspective is forgotten. Consider the American Indians, for example. From their point of view, they were just minding their own business when their land was invaded by boatloads of people from Europe. They tried to live in peace with the Europeans, but it didn't work because the newcomers wanted more and more land. For many years the Indians were portrayed as the bad guys in all of our history books. But were they really? Recently we've been able to read histories written from a Native American point of view. They have added a whole new dimension to our understanding of the past. The song "People of the Dawn" presents an Abenaki perspective on Rogers' Raid. A little girl who lived in Odanak at the time of the raid and saw what happened told her story to her children, and it was passed down from generation to generation. Compare her story with the story you read in textbooks.

People of the Dawn

We have been— here for so ver-y long, Since time un-known to an-y here.

Good hunt-ing for game be-side Lake Cham-plain, Good fish-ing in Mis-sis-quoi Bay.

Nzi - wal-dam, nzi-wal-dam,— A - nah-kwih-ka ndo-da-na,

Ma - lian pih-ta ozi-wal-dam— Nda to-mo wi-dom-ba.

We have been here for so very long
Since time unknown to any here
Good hunting for game beside Lake Champlain
Good fishing in Missisquoi Bay

In October seventeen-fifty-nine
Came orders to raid the town
Roger's Rangers came north to kill us all
And to burn Odanak down

Roger's Indian guide warned a young girl
"The Rangers hide, but I'm your friend
They come to burn your village down
Leave your home, they'll be here soon"

She ran to tell the Abenaki
"Hurry, they are on their way
To burn the village and kill us all
Hurry and run away"

Some listened and they sped away
Some said "She's just a child and I will stay"
They danced on all through the night
They were dead and gone before day

Nziwaldam, nziwaldam
Anahkwihka ndodana
Malian pihta oziwaldam
Nda tomo widomba

On this circle we sing this lonesome song
As we think of that sad day
Some of those who sped away
Came here to Missisquoi Bay

Nziwaldam, nziwaldam
Anahkwihka ndodana
Malian pihta oziwaldam
Nda tomo widomba

Translation of the Abenaki:
I am lonesome, I am lonesome
Our village grows up to trees
Marian is very lonesome
There is no friend anywhere

Pronunciation of the Abenaki:
Neh-ZEE-wall-dahm, neh-ZEE-wall-dahm
Ah-NOCK-we-kah neh-DOH-dah-nah
MOL-lee-ahn pee-TAH oh-ZEE-wall-dahm
Neh-DAH to-MAH WEE-dohm-bah

Margery Griswold, Indian Healer

Early white settlers learned much about the plant and animal life of Vermont from their Indian neighbors. Molly Orcutt was an Abenaki woman who was well known in the early 19th century for her treatment of dysentery with a concoction made from the inner bark of the spruce. Native remedies often combined a number of ingredients. A headache liniment, for example, consisted of white birch bark, hemlock bark, bear fat, and sperm from a buck deer boiled with onions, wild garlic, and molasses. Many of Vermont's early midwives were Indian or part Indian. It's not at all unusual, even today, to hear a Vermonter remark, "My grandmother was a full-blooded Indian and she knew all the herbs," or "My grandparents lived neighbor to an Indian couple and the wife taught my grandmother this recipe for poison ivy." Says Vermonter Russell Dwire, "My grandmother on my father's side was full-blooded Indian. I learned from my father all the different flowers and herbs in the woods, like ginseng, golden seal, and all that stuff. I've always felt that I got my love for the woods from the Indians and my grandmother."

The Randolph grade 5/6 team and Margaret read this story in Miriam Herwig's Randolph Beginnings. *Miriam also spoke to the students at the school. Further information came from Abby Hemenway's* Vermont, An Historical Gazetteer.

Randolph

Margery Griswold, Indian Healer

Jo - seph Gris - wold and his broth - ers, in sev - en - teen fif - ty - two, Sailed down the Con - nec - ti - cut in a ca - noe. The boat tipped o - ver and Jo - seph hit his head His broth - ers fought to save him but feared he was dead.

Joseph Griswold and his brothers, in seventeen-fifty-two
Sailed down the Connecticut in a canoe
The boat tipped over and Joseph hit his head
His brothers fought to save him but feared he was dead

For him could anything be done?
They ran to find the Indian Sachem
Though he was gone his daughter Margery they found
She learned the art of medicine from him

Margery saved Joseph with the magic she learned
The couple fell in love, for her hand Joseph yearned
Their families disapproved but they determined to wed
So married they were and to Randolph they fled

Seven kids they had here in Randolph Town
Benjamin, Frederick, Joseph, Lois, Sylvester, Eunice and John
Margery, herb woman, to whites and natives gave care
A familiar sight for years riding on her white mare

Margery rode out to a white man in need
In a snow storm that brought down her steed
She kept on walking although she was old
Poor Margery died from the chill we are told

Margery is remembered for healing and care
Riding through Randolph upon her white mare
The legend and love of the Griswolds live on
From their life story courage is drawn

Robert Sanford of Weybridge

Helen Freismuth's grade 5/6 wrote this song with Margaret, based on information from Ida Washington's book Carleton's Raid *and from an interview with her. Subsequently Ida included the song in* The History of Weybridge, Vermont. *Local folklore ascribes the name Lemon Fair to the lamentable affair of Carleton's raid.*

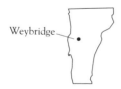

Weybridge

During the Revolutionary War the thirteen original colonies were fighting England for their independence. At that time Vermont was its own country, an independent republic. Vermont was right in the middle of the fighting — a dangerous place to be. The English were in Canada on our northern border and the new American nation was on our southern border. The English didn't want people to settle in Vermont, so they sent raiding parties south to destroy pioneer settlements and take settlers prisoner. These raids were organized by the English and carried out with the help of the Indians. A raiding party would appear without warning, take captives, burn buildings and destroy crops, then march their prisoners back to Canada. Most of these captives were later ransomed back to freedom. But some were adopted by native families and chose to stay on living with the Indians rather than return to their former lives. Many Vermont communities were raided during this period, including Royalton in 1780. When the Revolutionary War ended, the raids stopped and people were able to settle Vermont in peace.

Robert Sanford of Weybridge

Minor tune

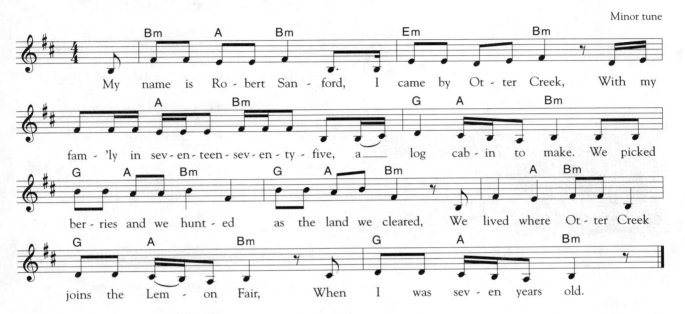

My name is Robert Sanford, I came by Otter Creek, With my fam'ly in seven-teen-seven-ty-five, a log cab-in to make. We picked berries and we hunt-ed as the land we cleared, We lived where Ot-ter Creek joins the Lem-on Fair, When I was sev-en years old.

My name is Robert Sanford, I came by Otter Creek
With my fam'ly in seventeen-seventy-five, a log cabin to make
We picked berries and we hunted as the land we cleared
We lived where Otter Creek joins the Lemon Fair
  When I was seven years old

I remember November, seventeen-seventy-eight
When Carleton's Raiders came down Otter Creek
They burnt houses and captured three boys and four men
Left girls, women and children in desolation
  When I was ten years old

On the way to Montreal when I took a serious fall
They left me in the forest, they took my dad and all
I walked back to Weybridge to find in the root cellar
My baby brother, Ira, my sister and my mother
  When I was ten years old

They were living on potatoes, for help I did seek
Barefooted I followed the icy banks of Otter Creek
I walked south fifteen miles or more 'til soldiers I did see
I brought them back to Weybridge to help my family and me
  When I was ten years old

Lucy Terry Prince

African Americans have a long history in Vermont. Their numbers have never been great, but they were among the first settlers. When Lucy Terry Prince came to Guilford in 1764, Vermont was still a frontier wilderness. Lucy Terry Prince was a very special person and is remembered today for the remarkable things that she did. In 1785 she went to Norwich, Vermont, to speak before the Governor's Council and ask for help against neighbors who were abusing her and her family. In Williamstown, Massachusetts, she debated with the board of trustees of a free academy that refused to admit her son because he was an African American. At the age of 67 she argued her side of a land dispute in court against a famous lawyer — and won her case! Other black Vermonters from long ago left few written records, so it's hard for historians to piece together what their lives were like. Census records can help. Every ten years since 1790 the U.S. Government has counted everyone in our country. Using these records, we can find out what people did for work. In the 1800s most African American men were farm laborers and most African American women worked as domestic servants. Although Vermont's constitution outlawed slavery, black people didn't seem to have the same opportunities as white people — even in Vermont. There were, of course, exceptions. When Alexander Twilight graduated from Middlebury College in 1823, he became the first black American to earn a college degree. He later founded and was headmaster of the Brownington Academy, a famous school in its day. Today African American Vermonters play an important role in the life of our state.

Margaret and Linda Bourne's grade 6 in Guilford read Lucy Terry Prince, *a paper by Linda Hecker. Lucy Terry and her husband, Abijah Prince, first moved to Guilford in 1764. Information about early Guilford came from* A Book of Country Things, Told by Walter Needham, Recorded by Barrows Mussey. *This is a condensation of a much longer song.*

Guilford

Lucy Terry Prince

Traditional tune: Streets of Derry

Chorus:
Come and follow the roads of Guilford
These same roads in Lucy Terry's day
Were footpaths, horse trails and tracks for wagons,
Where Lucy and 'Bijah made their way

Then brooks were dammed and mills were turning
For sawing logs and grinding grain
Shoemakers, coopers, tanners, hatters
Blacksmith forges, carding machines
Sledding goods to the Hub[1] in winter
Cheese, flax, hides, horn-combs, vinegar
To trade for rope, buttons, pins and needles
And for our bullets, lead and powder

Chorus

A pioneer woman from Deerfield
Lucy Terry earned a poet's fame
From Africa stolen to slavery
Until at last her freedom gained
Many years she lived in Guilford
Wrote poems and argued in a court of law
Married 'Bijah Prince and had nine children
First published black poet in America

Chorus

---

[1] Boston.

Crossett's Catamount

Cindy Lyon's grade 5/6 in Duxbury created this ballad from a true story found in a historical transcript called In Horse and Buggy Days, *written by a member of the Crossett Hill Association. Margaret and the students especially liked the first names of this early family of Crossetts, and came up with their own names for the team of horses.*

When Vermont was first settled, people were afraid of the wild animals that lived here. The settlers were moving into a land that was still a wilderness. It was the natural habitat of such creatures as bear and catamount and wolf. The settlers cleared land for farms and brought cows, pigs, and sheep up from southern New England. The catamount and other animals preyed on this livestock and occasionally even attacked people. When a pioneer settlement was troubled by an especially destructive animal, the men would band together to do something about it. They formed a posse — like in the "wild west" — only in this case the outlaw was an animal. The men spread out to make a huge circle around a section of forest. When the circle was complete, the leader fired three shots in the air, and everyone started walking toward the center. As the men moved forward, they banged on pans and rattled branches. This noise frightened the animals, and they ran from the men into the center of the circle. As the circle tightened, all of the animals would be trapped. Then the men could shoot the catamount or bear that had been causing trouble.

Crossett's Catamount

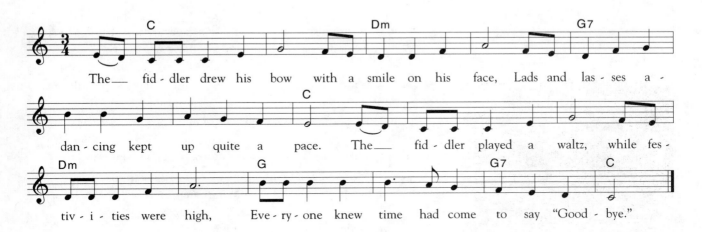

The — fid - dler drew his bow with a smile on his face, Lads and las - ses a - dan - cing kept up quite a pace. The — fid - dler played a waltz, while fes - tiv - i - ties were high, Eve - ry - one knew time had come to say "Good - bye."

The fiddler drew his bow with a smile on his face
Lads and lasses a-dancing kept up quite a pace
The fiddler played a waltz, while festivities were high
Everyone knew time had come to say "Good-bye"

They hitched horses to sleighs preparing to leave
Headed for home on a crisp winter eve
Janus Crossett, his wife Euretta and Armenta their babe
Ned and Dan a-pulling the sleigh

From out of the dark came two glowing eyes
Set upon by a catamount, they were terrified
Janus handed Euretta the reins
With babe in his arms faced the cat as it came

As the catamount neared the swift running sleigh
Janus pretended to throw baby away
The cat was kept off balance by the trick of his arm
Until they came to the shelter of their barn

Armed with a pitchfork they came to their home
Put Armenta to bed in a room all alone
They talked of their fright by the dim firelight
Went to join Armenta in the middle of the night

What they saw through the window made their hearts stand still
The catamount stood with his paws on the sill
They gave thanks as they saw that huge cat creep away
Janus, Euretta, and Armenta were safe

From Reuben Winchester's Autobiography

On Jay Stark's recommendation, John Esau's Junior Room (4/5) students borrowed Reuben Winchester's manuscript from the Marlboro Historical Society. The manuscript was fascinating, both because of Winchester's descriptions of his work as a boy and because of his language. Margaret and the students used his manner of speaking and, in many cases, his very words. Margaret said that his description of working the flax and tow is the best she has ever come across.

Marlboro

People don't use much linen today. But years ago it was important for clothing, sheets and pillowcases (they're still called bed linens), tablecloths, towels, and even grain bags. Linen was very strong and durable, but it was lots of work to make. Linen yarn is made from a plant called flax. When Vermont was first settled, people grew big gardens of flax to make linen. When they were ready to harvest, flax plants were pulled out by the roots and allowed to dry. After all the seeds were removed, they were "retted" or soaked by placing them in water until they began to stink. You know how the stems of flowers sometimes get black and slimy in a vase? When that happens to flax, it rots the bark away so you can get at the fibers in the stem. The stem fibers are the part of the plant that's used to make linen. Next the stems were crushed using a "flax break" to separate the fibers from the pulpy core. Then the flax was "scutched" or "swingled" to make the fibers soft and separate them from the short, coarse tow. Scutching was done by hanging the flax over the side of a board and striking it over and over again with a long wooden knife. Finally, the fibers were finished by drawing them through a series of metal combs called "hackles" or "hetchels". Then they were ready for

From Reuben Winchester's Autobiography

Minor tune

My name is Reuben Winchester, born in eighteen-twenty-five
On Higley Hill in Marlboro I was glad to be alive
As I was walking to school "When I was four years old past"
A great gander goose squawked, my brother's hand I clasped

As soon as I could ride a horse I took grist to Mather's mill
Corn, rye and wheat to grind, carried flour back to Higley Hill
From age twelve boys worked in summer as a general rule
They plowed and planted and mowed while others went to school

When my little sister Lois first began to spin
We made a wooden platform for her to walk back and forward on
Spinning, spinning fleece into yarn
For clothing in winter to keep us dry and warm

Father and we boys grew flax for weaving tow and linen
We did the breaking, swingling, hetcheling, girls did weaving and
    spinning[1]
They cooked and sewed, made butter and cheese, no time to play
Boys had "stints" in the fields bringing in the hay

My name is Reuben Winchester, born in eighteen-twenty-five
On Higley Hill in Marlboro I was glad to be alive

I bought a hen for 9 pence[2] with much too short legs
Though Father said she couldn't, she laid thirteen eggs
She laid them in the swingle tow[1], hatched every one she laid
In trading fourteen chickens, two dollars I was paid

I bartered for sheep with Rollin, took them home to Dad
Father said "That's the best trade that you ever made"
When I was 16 years old past, our crowded hive must swarm
I was the first to leave, with my trunk under my arm

My name is Reuben Winchester, born in eighteen-twenty-five
On Higley Hill in Marlboro I was glad to be alive

(The chorus is the same as the first two lines of the first verse and
can be inserted at will throughout the song.)

---

[1] The flax plant is first broken over heavy boards, then beaten
with a long wooden knife called a swingle to knock out coarse
particles, which are called swingle tow. The flax is then combed
with coarse, medium and fine hetchels. The coarse fibers are
woven into tow cloth, the fine into linen. Swingle tow was used
to pad horse collars. Nothing was wasted.

[2] Pence equals 12-1/2 cents.

Cambric Shirt

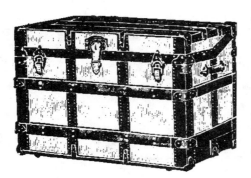

This song is from H.H. Flanders Ancient Ballads Traditionally Sung in New England, as contributed by Belle Luther Richards of Colebrook NH. It is one of the oldest songs in the English language, first appearing in print in 1673. In ancient versions, a false knight imposes three impossible tasks on a young girl. She evades the tasks and escapes from him by requiring that he perform tasks of equal difficulty first.

Try to imagine what it must have been like for the first colonists who came to North America from England in the early 1600s. They made a dangerous passage across a huge ocean to an unknown land. After they arrived, they were completely on their own, cut off from their families and neighbors and the familiar landscape of their English homeland. They weren't able to bring very much along, only the bare necessities for survival. They had to build a new life entirely from scratch, in the midst of a frightening wilderness. So they set about recreating what they had known at home, adapting it to their needs in the new world. They built the same kinds of houses and barns, laid out the same kinds of towns, and practiced the same kind of farming that they had grown up with in England. They may not have brought much baggage, but they brought lots of useful knowledge and experience. And this shaped their new lives here. The descendants of these English colonists were among those who settled Vermont and New Hampshire. They again brought many English traditions with them to their new home. One tradition that came along was the "Cambric Shirt," a song that had been sung in England for many hundreds of years. We still enjoy singing it in Vermont today!

Cambric Shirt

I want you to make me a cambric shirt
Blow, blow, blow ye winds, O
Without any thread or any needle work
The winds may blow your plaid away

I want you to wash it in a well
Blow, blow, blow ye winds, O
Where rains never were and water never fell
The winds may blow your plaid away

I want you to dry it on a thorn
Blow, blow, blow ye winds, O
That never bore blossom since Adam was born
The winds may blow your plaid away

(In response to the previous impossible tasks.)

Now you have asked me questions three
Blow, blow, blow ye winds, O
 I will ask as many of thee
The winds may blow your plaid away

I want you to plow me an acre of land
Blow, blow, blow ye winds, O
Between the salt water and the sea sand
The winds may blow your plaid away

I want you to plow it with a hog's horn
Blow, blow, blow ye winds, O
And sow it with a pepper corn
The winds may blow your plaid away

I want you to reap it with a scythe of leather
Blow, blow, blow ye winds, O
And rake it up with a hummingbird's feather
The winds may blow your plaid away

And when you have done this work
Blow, blow, blow ye winds, O
Come to me and you'll get your shirt
The winds may blow your plaid away

A Visit From Three Bears

Grade 5/6 students at the Randolph Village School created this ballad about schools and customs in Vermont pioneer days. All of our information came from Abby Hemenway's Vermont, An Historical Gazetteer. Using old fashioned phrases and wording from the original account, Margaret and the students imagined that they were there.

Randolph

When the settlers from southern New England first moved into the Vermont wilderness, they were quick to establish free public schools. In those early days, Vermont schools were established in districts. A district was formed when a group of neighbors got together, built a school, and hired a teacher. The rule of thumb was that no child should have to walk more than three miles to school, so each neighborhood had a school. The number and location of schools varied as the town's population grew or declined. Come rain or shine, children rose early to do their morning chores and then headed off to school, carrying their lunches with them. Says Katharine DuClos, of Braintree, of her childhood: "Dad always told us that we weren't sugar or salt, and no matter the weather we walked just the same. I waded through drifts up onto Braintree Hill, to the little red schoolhouse there a good many times. We never missed a day unless we were pretty sick."

A Visit From Three Bears

Mixolydian tune

On one cold win-ter morn-ing two hun-dred years a-go, School mas-ter Pe-rez Tra-cy came a-trudg-ing through the snow, Toward a small school-house— made of logs so sound For the chil-dren of the eight fam'-lies who lived three miles a-round. For the chil-dren of the eight fam'-lies who lived three miles a-round.

On one cold winter morning two hundred years ago
School master Perez Tracy came a-trudging through the snow
Toward a small schoolhouse made of logs so sound
For the children of the eight fam'lies who lived three miles around
For the children of the eight fam'lies who lived three miles around

He'd build a fire in the huge fireplace to make the room all warm
For the children as they came pulled by ox sled in the storm
He thought some kids were in the room, he found the door ajar
But when he stepped in, he was wrong by far
But when he stepped in, he was wrong by far

Three bears were in the schoolhouse, a mother and two cubs
He sprang to the hearth, grabbed a shovel for a club
He commenced a regular fight, the work it got quite warm
When Diah Flint arrived with a muzzle loaded gun
When Diah Flint arrived with a muzzle loaded gun

Diah Flint dispatched the bears, then help he went to find
They hung the bears, got them skinned and dressed by nine
As scholars arrived they distributed the meat
Fam'lies rejoiced that night for they had meat to eat
Fam'lies rejoiced that night for they had meat to eat

The children reveled in doughnuts fried in bear grease
Perez Tracy tanned the cub skins, his true love to please
He made a bearskin cape for Diah's sister Olive Flint
When Olive wore the cape to church, townspeople got the hint
When Olive wore the cape to church, townspeople got the hint

Perez and Olive were in love, they married the next spring
They lived on the Ridge Road, their story we do sing
"It's all because of the bear cape" we heard Polly Hebard say
This couple they lived happily all of their days
This couple they lived happily all of their days

The Missing Talented Traveling Builder

When settlers from southern New England first came to Vermont, they went about building their houses much differently than we do today. They had no bulldozers or backhoes. Their heavy equipment was a team of oxen to move stones or to drag logs down out of the forest. They dug the basement of a new house by hand, piled stones without mortar for the foundation, and built a stone base for the fireplace and oven. Large logs were squared off and cut to length. These were used as posts and beams to frame the house. Posts were set up at each corner to support a framework of beams that carried the second floor. Beams were cut with tongues that fit into grooves cut in other beams. Each joint was fastened in place with a wooden peg. This held the structure together. Builders used axes, saws, chisels, and planes to shape the wood. It was a handmade world back then. The door latches and hinges, even the nails, were handcrafted by a local blacksmith. No wonder these houses have lasted 200 years.

Helen Renner came to school and told this tale to Margaret and the Pownal fourth graders. It has been passed down in Helen's family for generations. She lives in the house, which has stood since the time of the military musters before the Revolution. It was probably her great-grandfather who moved the barn when he bought the place in 1840. Today the chestnut oaks referred to in the song are rare in Pownal.

Pownal

The Missing Talented Traveling Builder

Minor tune

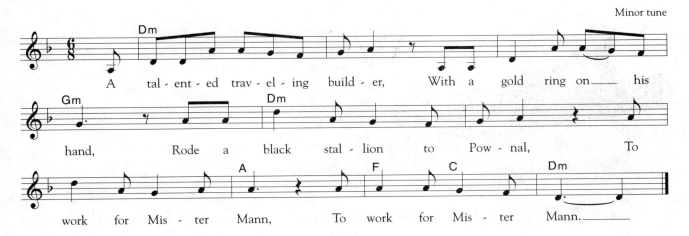

A tal-ent-ed trav-el-ing build-er, With a gold ring on his hand, Rode a black stal-lion to Pow-nal, To work for Mis-ter Mann, To work for Mis-ter Mann.

A talented traveling builder
With a gold ring on his hand
Rode a black stallion to Pownal
To work for Mister Mann
To work for Mister Mann

To build an inn for travelers
Two hundred years ago
And two barns for the animals
The work was hard and slow
The work was hard and slow

He dug the cellar, laid up stone
Hewed beams from chestnut oak trees
That oxen pulled from the mountains
The oxen worked in teams
The oxen worked in teams

He built a big stone oven
A fire those stones would heat
To bake pies and beans and cornbread
For travelers who came to eat
For travelers who came to eat

And to feed the farmers
Minutemen volunteers
Who came to Mr. Mann's farm
To muster twice a year
To muster twice a year

Said the talented traveling builder
"Mr. Mann my work is done"
He asked for his pay on his very last day
But money he got none
But money he got none

For the talented traveling builder
Disappeared, left his horse behind
When eighty years later they moved the barn
His body they did find
His body they did find

Skeleton with its head bashed in
Since the day he got no pay
Gold ring upon his finger
Under the barn he lay
Under the barn he lay

Thomas and Elizabeth Chittenden

Thomas Chittenden was Vermont's first governor. In his day there were no appointment secretaries, limousines, or state police escorts. Once, when the governor traveled to attend the legislature, he ended up sharing his bed with a pig! Today the state capital is Montpelier. The state house is where the legislature meets and the governor has his office. It's the big building with the gold dome. Back when Vermont was a new republic, Vermont's government had no home. Each time the legislature met, it was in a different town. One time it met in Charlestown, New Hampshire, which isn't even in Vermont! For a while Windsor and Rutland were designated the east and west capitals, so that people on both sides of the Green Mountains would have equal treatment. But later the legislature moved around again — everyone wanted the capital in their town. Sessions met in Vergennes, Middlebury, Newbury, Burlington, Westminster, Danville, and Woodstock. Finally, in 1805 the legislators fixed the capital at Montpelier, a town where they'd never met before. After 30 years of moving around, our state government finally had a permanent home.

Guided by Margaret, a multi-aged team of 12 Williston students created this song. They read passages from A History of the Town of Williston and from Abby Hemenway's Vermont, An Historical Gazetteer to find these insights into the character of this famous couple. Although the chorus can be sung after each verse, Margaret likes to sing the last four verses without interruption, as they tell a good story.

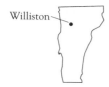

Williston

Thomas and Elizabeth Chittenden

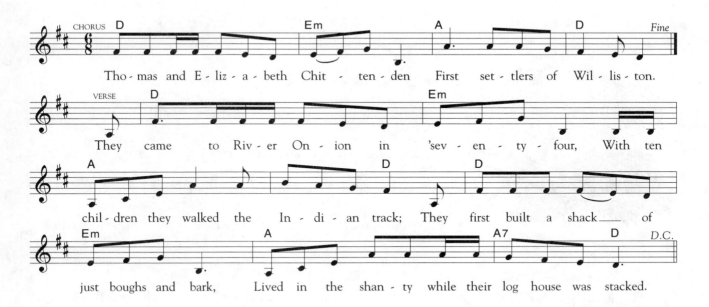

Thomas and Elizabeth Chittenden
First settlers of Williston

They came to River Onion in 'seventy-four
With ten children they walked the Indian track
They first built a shack of just boughs and bark
Lived in the shanty while their log house was stacked

Thomas and Elizabeth Chittenden
First settlers of Williston

When Elizabeth blew the dinner horn
The workers were able to come to the table
To eat with Thomas and Elizabeth and all the rest
Even the most important guests

Thomas and Elizabeth Chittenden
First settlers of Williston

One night when Thomas was out in a storm
A welcome log cabin came in sight
He knocked at the door, when the farmer came out
He asked for a lodging for the night

One bed was all that stood in the room
With a fireplace, a door, by the corner a loom
He refused the bed to lay down his head
So under her loom the wife made his bed

In came a shoat[1] by the light of the moon
Thomas just rolled over and fell asleep soon
He crept out in the morning, left the pig in his bed
And dropped a crown[2] where he had laid his head

Next day the farmer at the legislature
Was awestruck to see Thomas as governor
He apologized for the pig in the bed
"I had a good laugh" was what Thomas said

Thomas and Elizabeth Chittenden
First settlers of Williston

---

[1] A young hog.
[2] A gold coin.

The Ballad of Aaron Rising and the Wolves

This ballad was written with Suzanne Dirmaier's fifth grade class in Warren. The information came from Mary Blair's unpublished manuscript in the Warren Library. Tripp Johnson, a student, found that Aaron Rising lived from 1786 to 1871 and is buried in the East Warren Cemetery.

Katharine Flint DuClos tells a story about her ancestor, William Flint, coming to Vermont in the 1780s: "He came in the wintertime with a sled. And they had a little three year old girl. And they drove an ox and a cow. And all the way up through, they used the milk from that cow for that little girl. And they settled way up on Braintree Hill and they built a cabin there." The white settlers' first few years were often very difficult. They came to a wilderness of unbroken forest and had to build a life from scratch. After they had a place to live, they set about clearing land. It took several years to completely clear a field, and in the meantime they did the best they could. Potatoes and squash grew vigorously even under less-than-perfect conditions. When all else failed, these were the foods that kept people alive. The best known time of hardship was 1816, "a year without summer." There were frosts every month that year and many discouraged people left Vermont for good.

Warren

The Ballad of Aaron Rising and the Wolves

Traditional tune

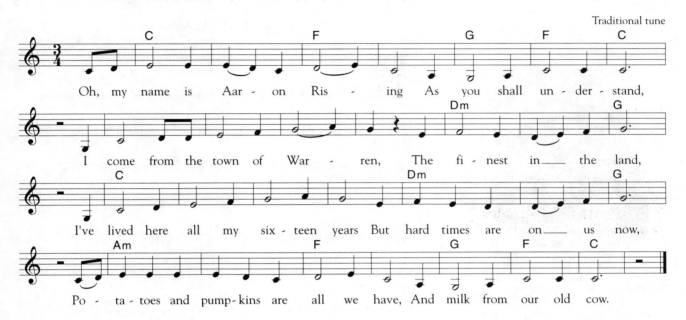

Oh, my name is Aar - on Ris - ing As you shall un - der - stand,

I come from the town of War - ren, The fi - nest in___ the land,

I've lived here all my six - teen years But hard times are on___ us now,

Po - ta - toes and pump - kins are all we have, And milk from our old cow.

Oh, my name is Aaron Rising
As you shall understand
I come from the town of Warren
The finest in the land
I've lived here all my sixteen years
But hard times are on us now
Potatoes and pumpkins are all we have
And milk from our old cow

Now potatoes and pumpkins are very nice
But we need something more
Over the mountain in Randolph Town
The miller has grain in store
Ma said "Boys take the axe
And cut the birch trees down
We'll burn the logs, then soak the ash
Then gather the liquid in"

In the big iron pot on a wooden crane
O'er a fire we simmered it down
'Til we had enough salts to barter for grain
With the miller in Randolph Town
I loaded the potash onto the old mare
And I wore my pants of tow
And hungry, along the rough mountain trail
To Roxbury I did go

Only potatoes and pumpkin in Roxbury
So hungry I'll push on
To Braintree, but it's still the same
So on to Randolph Town
"Miller, miller do you hear
I have potash to barter with you"
But three bushels of grain was all he'd give
For others were hungry too

He gave me the balance in money
Weary and hungry I started home
Still to shy to ask for food
I'll go back for potatoes and pumpkin
But every farm that I passed by
All the lights were out
Nearly starved I still pushed on
But howling wolves were about

There was one to the north, one to the south,
One to the east and west
"If they get me now it will soon be over
And it will be for the best"
But I jumped on the back of my tired old mare
And still we pushed on
Until at last came the wondrous dawn
And the howling wolves were gone

At sunrise I dragged the meal to the house
Climbed to the loft to bed
Ma would bake a johnny cake[1]
At breakfast I would be fed
But when she called me down
At last came tears of despair
I wept at the sight of the meager piece
But Ma said it was my share

---

[1] A bread made from cornmeal, flour, eggs, and milk.

Song of the Ages,
Georgia's Davis Cemetery

In the Davis Cemetery directly behind the Georgia school, Susan Kreps and her grade 5 students spent some time studying the stones, then sat quietly for a long time imagining what life had been like for those early settlers. With Margaret, they read in the Georgia Town History of the spinning and dyeing of wool, the making of butter and cheese and the building of cabins. Mrs. Kreps came in one morning all excited — she had dreamed the chorus, and so the song was complete.

Georgia

Before children can start school nowadays they have to have lots of shots: DPT (diphtheria, pertussis, tetanus), measles, mumps, and rubella, and the polio vaccine, which you drink. These are immunizations. They make your body produce antibodies so you won't get these diseases if you are exposed to them. Most other diseases can easily be treated with antibiotics. If you do happen to catch one, it isn't serious. This wasn't always so. When today's grandpas and grandmas were children, there were no antibiotics and no immunizations for many of these diseases. If a child caught scarlet fever, all the parents could do was pack him or her with ice and wait until the fever ran its course. Some children recovered without any problems. Others became blind or deaf. Still others died. (In the 1800s a smallpox epidemic might sweep through a community, and every family would lose loved ones.) Next time you walk through an old cemetery, notice the graves of children. In the East Roxbury Cemetery the names of brothers are carved on linked headstones with the message, "6 hours difference in their deaths."

Song of the Ages, Georgia's Davis Cemetery

Minor tune

We strolled through Davis Cemetery, The last day of September, On a crisp and sunny day; Our time there we'll remember.

Oh, the wind sang a song of the ages As we sat by those old stones, It told of the life of young Georgia, And we knew that we were not alone.

We strolled through Davis Cemetery
The last day of September
On a crisp and sunny day
Our time there we'll remember

Chorus:
Oh the wind sang a song of the ages
As we sat by those old stones
It told of the life of young Georgia
And we knew that we were not alone

On our journey we sat a-thinking
Of people who lived long ago
We walked easy by tilted stones
Marble, slate, granite also

Chorus

Nancy, did you churn the butter
Did you press the cheese?
Sarah, did you pick the sumac
To dye wool that you spun from fleece?

Chorus

Thomas, did you cut the timber
With your axe to clear these fields?
Titus, did you build your cabin
And grind your corn into meal?

Chorus

We sing of those three pretty babies
Who lie under their triple stone
Hannah and Manchester's children
For ages their names unknown

Chorus

Our Two Hands:
Work in Early Huntington

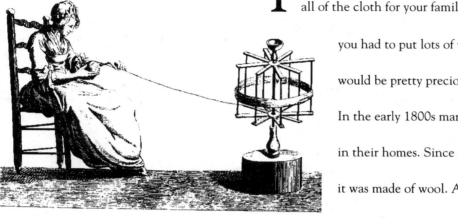

To create this song, Margaret and Grace Freeman's grade 3/4 at the Brewster Pierce School in Huntington used information from Abby Hemenway's Vermont, An Historical Gazetteer. The interesting account of early days in Huntington was written in 1860 by James John, son of Jehiel John, first settler of the area.

Huntington —

Think of all the clothing you wear. Imagine having to make all of the cloth for your family's shirts, pants, and dresses. If you had to put lots of work into making that cloth, it would be pretty precious. And years ago cloth was.

In the early 1800s many people made cloth on looms in their homes. Since sheep were common, much of it was made of wool. After the sheep were sheared, the fleece was washed and the sticks and burrs were picked out of it. Then tufts of fleece then were carded using two flat wire-toothed brushes called carding combs. Carding made each of the little hair fibers go in the same direction. It was slow work. Wool came off the carding combs in a long fluffy rope called a roving. Using a large spinning wheel, which was turned by hand, the roving was twisted into a strong, continuous yarn. This was wound around the arms of a clock reel (which looked like a little windmill) and measured into skeins. The yarn was then ready for weaving. It might take several months to prepare enough yarn for clothing or a blanket.

Our Two Hands: Work in Early Huntington

Traditional tune: Ranodine

We cleared our land by Lincoln Hill, Took our ax - es and start - ed chop-pin'; Hewed those beams 'til they were square, Then we had a house rais - in'. For a bench, split a log, put four holes in the bot - tom, In those four holes put sticks. La - ter we chopped down trees to bar - ter For chairs made by Jon - a - than Dix. We worked with our two hands.

We cleared our land by Lincoln Hill
Took our axes and started choppin'
Hewed those beams 'til they were square
Then we had a house raisin'
For a bench, split a log, put four holes in the bottom
In those four holes put sticks
Later we chopped down trees to barter
For chairs made by Jonathan Dix
We worked with our two hands

We tanned our cowhide for pairs of boots
Made by shoemaker Ben Brownell
Ma traded flax to Asa Gillette
He made her a spinning wheel
We sheared the sheep and cleaned the wool
Ma spun wool, linen and tow
Wove blankets for to keep us warm
Knit socks and wove cloth for clothes
We worked with our two hands

In boxes made in the cheese box factory
To market we'd send our cheese
Along with butter and eggs
And honey from our bees
Feathers from our chickens and geese
Gave featherbeds and pillows
In summertime we raised our grain
In fall took it to the mill
We worked with our two hands

The Ballad of Devil's Hill

This tale comes from an old letter in the Fairbanks Museum in St. Johnsbury, which was given to Kathy Holmes' grade 5/6 in Peacham by Charlie Brown. Margaret and the students used phrases from the old letter and added some local history concerning early settlement and drinking habits. Simeon Walker was born in 1756.

Peacham

Modern legends are told as true stories all around the country — about mouse tails in soft drinks, Elvis Presley sightings, or crocodiles in city sewer systems. Katharine DuClos recounts an old-time legend set in the town of Braintree: "One night, many years ago, Ashbel Tucker dreamed three times that he walked down to Ayer's Brook and saw a strange man there. The man told Ashbel that he'd buried a pot of money nearby. After the third dream Ashbel woke up, jumped out of bed, went down to the brook, and there was the man! Going home he met a neighbor and told him about his dream. His neighbor knew a Northfield man who could locate metal with a dowsing rod. So they got the dowser and he found the money pot. But when they started to dig, the pot scooted away, lifting the dirt to show which way it had gone. Every time Ashbel and his neighbor found it, the pot got away. Later, several men tried together. When they found the pot, they stuck scythe blades down into the ground all around it so that it couldn't escape. Silas Flint Jr. thought he was the one who should be rich. He pulled up one of the scythes and away went the pot! After that, people came to dig in the night until John Hutchinson forbade digging on his farm." All around Vermont you'll hear legends about buried treasure, haunted houses, and, of course, Champ, the Lake Champlain monster. Are they fact or fiction?

The Ballad of Devil's Hill

Dorian tune

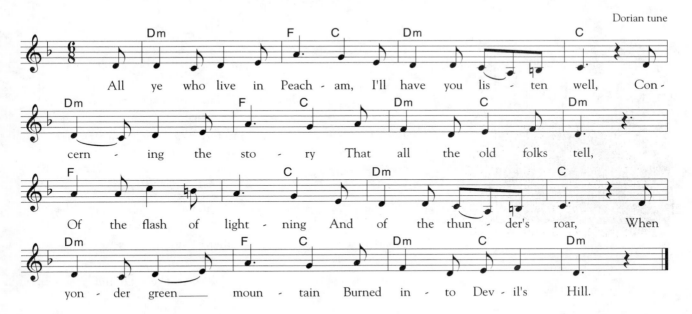

All ye who live in Peach-am, I'll have you lis-ten well, Con-cern-ing the sto-ry That all the old folks tell, Of the flash of light-ning And of the thun-der's roar, When yon-der green mountain Burned in-to Dev-il's Hill.

All ye who live in Peacham
I'll have you listen well
Concerning the story
That all the old folks tell
Of the flash of lightning
And of the thunder's roar
When yonder green mountain
Burned into Devil's Hill

Up from the Connecticut
The early settlers came
From Newbury to Peacham
They followed the spotted line
Along an early Indian trail
To make their pitch they strode
In later days the path they trod
Became Bailey-Hazen Road

Up the Bailey-Hazen
As the old century turned
Wandered a wild and haggard man
All company he spurned
Simeon Walker gave him leave
To build upon his land
A shop where he could live, his work
No one could understand

From whence he came nobody knew
Nor what he did at night
For five years from his chimney
Glowed a mysterious light
Are you an inventor? Counterfeiter?
Alchemist? Silver into gold?
Old Miers, are you a wizard
Or have you sold your soul?

There were eight stills in Peacham
One near Walker's farm
From seventy pounds potatoes
Comes five gallons potato rum
At David Elkin's tavern
A-drinking one night in the fall
Jonathan Elkins, Simeon Walker, Joel Blanchard
Captain Bailey and all

A clap of violent thunder
And then a blaze of light
Stupefied by the shock or the whiskey
These men saw a fearsome sight
A figure holding a fiery brand
Went flying through the air
To sink in the bog with a terrible hiss
Then nothing more was there

And nothing but ashes could ever be
    found
Where Miers and his cabin had been
Nought but a pile of mossy stones
In the forest can be seen
An eminence above the bog that night
Was scarred by heat and by flame
Since that time so long ago
Devil's Hill has been its name

The Ballad of Charles Swift and His Dog

This true story by Pat Koledo's 3/4 class was inspired by James John's 1860 writing in Abby Hemenway's Vermont, An Historical Gazetteer. The students gave names to the horse and the dog and dressed Charles Swift in the garb described in the song Fifty Years Ago.

Huntington

M ost towns in Vermont were chartered by a group of investors called proprietors. These men paid the state (or the English governor) for the right to survey and divide the town into lots, which they could sell at a profit. They were Vermont's first developers. Mills were so important in pioneer Vermont that the proprietors often would give a miller 100 free acres of land just for settling in that town. The miller was the backbone of the community. He ground the settlers' grain to make the flour and meal they needed to feed themselves and their livestock. Our ancestors used rushing water as an energy source to run things. So they built their mills next to a river or stream and made a dam to divert the water and turn the large mill wheel. As the mill wheel went around, it turned granite grindstones that crushed and ground the kernels of grain. As payment, the miller took his "toll" by keeping some of the ground grain for himself. There are abandoned mill sites throughout the state.

The Ballad of Charles Swift and His Dog

Minor tune

Chorus:
Oh, the mill wheel is turning around and round
Down on the Huntington River
By these two huge grindstones our grain is ground
Down on the Huntington River

In the month of December, eighteen-twenty-four
When I was twelve years old
In my tow pants and knit socks and cowhide boots
I left Camel's Hump in the cold
Pa said "Take horse Thunderbolt down to the mill
Get the wheat and corn and buckwheat ground"
Out to the barn, took down the saddle
But this is what I found

Continued on next page

The Ballad of Charles Swift and His Dog

Continued from previous page

I found one stirrup on, but one stirrup gone
Replaced it with a strap of looped leather
Loaded on the grain in sacks of tow
Called dog Benjie and we went on together
Down at the mill I unload the sacks
"Miller I need this ground"
Into the hopper he pours the grain
And the big old wheel goes round

Oh, the mill wheel is turning around and round
Down on the Huntington River
By these two huge grindstones our grain is ground
Down on the Huntington River

From the flour the miller took his share of toll
From every bushel he took one peck
I put the rest on Thunderbolt, called to my dog
And then we started back
The horse made a bolt with a sudden leap
Threw me from my seat clear
But my foot caught fast in the strap
And I was filled with fear

I was filled with fear that my head might drag
But quick as a flash
Old dog Benjie caught the collar of my coat
Carried me as the wild horse dashed
One hundred rods he kept me from the ground
Benjie saved my life and limb
My name is Charles Swift and as long as I live
I'll always be grateful to him

Oh, the mill wheel is turning around and round
Down on the Huntington River
By these two huge grindstones our grain is ground
Down on the Huntington River

Vermont in the 19th Century

Fifty Years Ago

Fifty Years Ago is from the H.H. Flanders Collection at Middlebury College, as sung by Susan Estes of Bennington in 1941. In the ballads, Aaron Rising and the Wolves, and Charles Swift and His Dog, the students had the boys dressed in tow pants as they rode to the mill.

When older people look back on their lives they always see lots of changes, no matter what era they live in. Today's grandmas and grandpas remember a time when horses were used to do farm work and when people heated and cooked with wood. Now farms have tractors (some farms even have computer feeders), most homes are heated by an oil furnace, and people cook on gas or electric stoves. These are big changes and they've all happened in a single lifetime. The song *Fifty Years Ago* records the changes of a single lifetime — a lifetime lived long, long ago. This song looks back on a time when families made the change from spinning their own yarn and weaving their own wool and linen cloth to buying factory-made cloth at the store. And it was the era when woodstoves were introduced. People were pretty skeptical of them at first — open fireplaces had been used for cooking and heating for generations. It was also a time when the oxen used by the pioneer generation were replaced by a team of horses, and the rough wagon and sled were set aside for a fancy buggy and sleigh. Have you ever heard an older person remark, "What is the world coming to?" Their grandma or grandpa probably said the same thing.

Fifty Years Ago

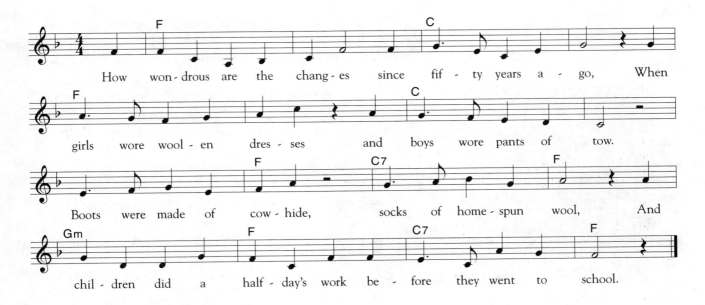

How won-drous are the chang-es since fif-ty years a-go, When

girls wore wool-en dres-ses and boys wore pants of tow.

Boots were made of cow-hide, socks of home-spun wool, And

chil-dren did a half-day's work be-fore they went to school.

How wondrous are the changes since fifty years ago
When girls wore woolen dresses and boys wore pants of tow[1]
Boots were made of cowhide, socks of homespun wool
And children did a half day's work before they went to school

When girls took music lessons upon the spinning wheel
They practiced late and early on spindle, swift and reel
Boys they rode so far to mill, a dozen miles or so
And hurried off before 'twas day, fifty years ago

Well do I remember that Wilson Benton Stove
That father bought and paid for in cloth us girls had wove
People how they wondered when we got the thing to go
They swore 'twould burst and kill us all, fifty years ago

When people rode to meeting in sleds instead of sleighs
And wagons rode as easy as buggys nowadays
Oxen answered well for teams 'though now they'd be too slow
For people lived not half so fast, fifty years ago

Yes, every thing has altered, I cannot tell the cause
Man is always tampering with nature's wondrous laws
What on earth we're coming to does anybody know
For every thing has changed so much since fifty years ago

[1]A coarse cloth made from flax.

The Road to Hackadam

Ghost towns are mysterious and scary. There are lots of them out west where tumbleweed blows down the main streets and open doors creak in the wind. There are ghost towns in Vermont, too.

From the writings of Ruth Best and Mary Spargo, students in grade 5/6 learned of this mysterious and deserted part of West Haven. It had once had great potential as a settlement before Lake Champlain silted up at the southern end. West Haven was a thriving manufacturing town when all of the mills were running, and was a distribution point for Terry Mantel Clocks. There are still secret rooms in some of the big houses that were used to hide run away slaves before and during the Civil War.

It's hilly in central Vermont, and the towns there were first settled on the hilltops. In the town of Braintree, long ago, the town hall, church, burying ground, clerk's office, town pound, store, school, and hotel all clustered around a busy intersection on the top of Braintree Hill. The forest had been cleared and roads ran off in all directions, lined with enterprising farms. Today, Braintree Hill has returned to forest. The church and burying ground are still there, but the church is a museum and the burying ground is full. The town hall, the clerk, the school, and all of the businesses have moved down into the valley. But there's evidence of that earlier time if you know where to look for it. Deep in the forest you'll find cellar holes with roses and rhubarb growing nearby or a stone bridge for a road leading nowhere.

West Haven

The Road to Hackadam

Traditional tune: Miller of Dee

As I walked out one evening in weather fine and fair, All around me there was magic and myst'ry in the air. And what I saw that night was of the days long gone, As I strolled toward the river on the road to Hack-a-dam, As I strolled toward the river on the road to Hack-a-dam.

As I walked out one evening in weather fine and fair
All around me there was magic and myst'ry in the air
And what I saw that night was of the days long gone
As I strolled toward the river on the road to Hackadam
As I strolled toward the river on the road to Hackadam

There by Carver's Falls I saw to my surprise
A gristmill grinding grain before my very eyes
A sawmill too was running on power from the falls
And below I saw the river filled with boats from the canals
And below I saw the river filled with boats from the canals

Canal boats bound for Albany, from the Falls to Whitehall
To Fort Edward and the Hudson through the Champlain Canal
Carrying shoes made from the tanyard's leather, butter, eggs, and
   cheese
And cloth from the woolen mill woven from West Haven fleece
And cloth from the woolen mill woven from West Haven fleece

I heard the clatter of the looms there by the woolen mill
Where the Hubbardton joins the Poultney, those looms were
   never still
And further along the river I saw Hackadam
A town all laid out in squares, someone's dream and plan
A town all laid out in squares, someone's dream and plan

A black man and woman and child were in a boat, a young girl
   rowed
Taking them to a station of the Underground Railroad
In a West Haven home with hidden hideaways
They were on their way north to Canada to never more be slaves
They were on their way north to Canada to never more be slaves

Back up the hill I saw the house of Dr. Simeon Smith
With a Terry Mantel Clock over the mantlepiece
The clock struck twelve, midnight, I knew the spell was broken
But I'll always remember the road to Hackadam
But I'll always remember the road to Hackadam

Eagle Square

Kathy Link, Shaftsbury's Arts and Basics Program Director, inspired teams of students to ask questions of older residents of the town. From local historian Eugene Kosche they learned of the invention of the carpenter's square and of the history of one of the oldest factories in Vermont, still in operation today as a branch of Stanley Tools. Six students from Bill Colvin's Grade 6 collaborated with Margaret in making this song.

Shaftsbury

Blacksmiths used to be the 'fix-it men' of their communities. They knew how to work with both iron and wood to make the things that farmers needed. Shoeing horses was only one of their jobs. They could also fabricate water tubs, bob sleds, and farm wagons from scratch. A blacksmith could shape a formless piece of iron into a doorlatch, a hinge, or a nail. If you needed an iron tool for a special job, the blacksmith could make it to your specifications. If something broke and you needed a special part, he could match it. Buggy and wagon wheels were made of wood but had a metal "tire" which could take the wear and tear. If a tire came off or needed replacing, it was a job for a blacksmith. As George Daniels explains, "You heat the tire up red hot, drop it on to the wheel, then throw water on it fast. It shrinks it quick, shrinks it down and makes it tight." When Vermonters first started buying automobiles, there were no garage mechanics. It was the blacksmith who had the tools, knowledge, and skill to work on this newfangled invention. According to George Daniels, "Blacksmith shops turned into garages. That's where the mechanics were, in blacksmith shops."

Eagle Square

Traditional tune: Cambric Shirt

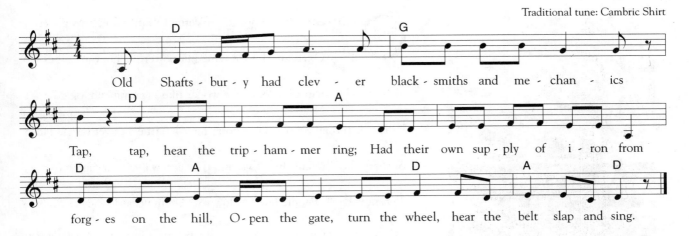

Old Shafts-bur-y had clev-er black-smiths and me-chan-ics

Tap, tap, hear the trip-ham-mer ring; Had their own sup-ply of i-ron from

forg-es on the hill, O-pen the gate, turn the wheel, hear the belt slap and sing.

Old Shaftsbury had clever blacksmiths and mechanics
Tap, tap, hear the trip hammer ring
Had their own supply of iron from forges on the hill
Open the gate, turn the wheel, hear the belt slap and sing

A pedlar came to town, needed shoes for his pony
Tap tap hear the trip hammer ring
Saw the sign of blacksmith Silas Hawes
Open the gate, turn the wheel, hear the belt slap and sing

He shod the pony and he fixed the cart
Tap tap hear the trip hammer ring
Took in barter two old used saws
Open the gate, turn the wheel, hear the belt slap and sing

Held up the saws, welded a right angle
Tap tap hear the trip hammer ring
Cut and ground and smoothed and polished
Open the gate, turn the wheel, hear the belt slap and sing

About eighteen-fifteen Silas Hawes made the square
Tap tap hear the trip hammer ring
Other men from Bennington joined to make more
Open the gate, turn the wheel, hear the belt slap and sing

In eighteen-fifty-nine they formed a company, Eagle Square
Tap tap hear the trip hammer ring
Undershot water wheel from Paran Creek gave power
Open the gate, turn the wheel, hear the belt slap and sing

Builder's work came easy with our squares ground thick to thin
Tap tap hear the trip hammer ring
Squares went out by cart or sleigh to Troy and down the Hudson
Open the gate, turn the wheel, hear the belt slap and sing

The factory and Eagle Square Stamps[1] are still here
Tap tap hear the trip hammer ring
Many generations have worked at Eagle Square
Open the gate, turn the wheel, hear the belt slap and sing

---

[1] A metal stamp for identifying manufacturer of tools.

Grandpa Crossett's Oxen

Oxen were very important on Vermont farms for many generations. Oxen are slow-moving but powerful. They are especially good for winter work in the woods like sugaring and logging — better even than horses. They don't have a harness to get tangled in or sharp shoes to cut their legs, and they can wallow through most any snow bank. People like to plow with them because they're slow and steady, and it's easy to drive them. But they aren't as good in hot weather. The flies bother them, and they're likely to panic and run away. You have to be very calm, patient, and consistent to train an ox. Only a very responsible boy or girl would be trusted with that job. First you teach them to stop and start, then to turn to the left and right. By the time they are full grown, they're broken in and ready for farm work. Lots of grandmas and grandpas remember how much fun it was to work with oxen when they were kids.

While factual information came from In Horse and Buggy Days, *written by a member of the Duxbury Crossett Hill Association, Margaret Morse's grade 2/3 and Sara Barrett's grade 2 used their collective knowledge and imaginations to make a mental picture of the old ways on the farm. One student contacted a farmer to find out what the oxen might have been called and the meaning of "nigh" and "off" ox.*

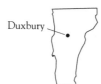

Duxbury

Grandpa Crossett's Oxen

Once up-on a time— on— Grand-pa Cros-sett's farm, He— had a yoke of ox-en he

kept out in the barn. Tom and Jer-ry pulled the big two-wheeled ox cart, Paired—

up by the ox yoke, they worked from dawn 'til dark, On Grand-pa Cros-sett's farm.

Once upon a time on Grandpa Crossett's farm
He had a yoke of oxen he kept out in the barn
Tom and Jerry pulled the big two-wheeled ox cart
Paired up by the ox yoke they worked from dawn 'til dark
On Grandpa Crossett's farm

In the winter they were logging, in the summer hauling hay
Gathering sap in the spring, go to market one fall day
Barter eggs and cheese and butter for mirrors, knives and pots
Tom was the "nigh" and Jerry the "off" ox
On Grandpa Crossett's farm

Tom on the left and Jerry on the right
Pulling stones with all their might
Digging cellars and hauling beams
For building houses, a handy team
On Grandpa Crossett's farm

Uncle Rob McAllister in his 1910 machine
Stalled on Mill Hill, tipped over, car did lean
Grandpa yoked up Tom and Jerry, pulled the car half a mile
So proud of his team, he wore a big smile
On Grandpa Crossett's farm

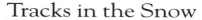

Tracks in the Snow

Recognizing animal tracks used to be a basic survival skill. Many generations of Vermont children learned to identify the tracks of fox, weasel, mink, rabbit, and coyote. Trapping was an important part of everyday life. Animal skins were often a ready source of much-needed cash. Children walked trap lines with their parents, learning the ways of the forest by example. Boys in school often had their own trap lines to check. Imagine getting up before dawn to hike several miles through marsh and forest — before morning chores and the long walk to school! As life-long trapper Russell Dwire observes, "The first thing in trapping is to know what animal makes what track. You've got to be able to tell a mink track from a cat track. Or a dog track from a coyote. If you don't, you're apt to catch your neighbor's dog or cat. That could be embarrassing."

Margaret began this song with a verse and tune that she learned from Olive MacArthur, her husband's mother. She and the first grade students in Sherburne and in Fair Haven let their thoughts wander out into the snow for more tracks, making up rhymes as they went along.

Sherburne
Fair Haven

Tracks in the Snow

Oh, what fun-ny lit-tle tracks in the snow, Don't you won-der what they are, where they go? I think a bun-ny rab-bit white Hopped a-cross the snow last night, Oh, what fun-ny lit-tle tracks in the snow.

Oh, what funny little tracks in the snow
Don't you wonder what they are, where they go?
I think a bunny rabbit white
Hopped across the snow last night
Oh, what funny little tracks in the snow

Oh, what funny little tracks in the snow
Don't you wonder what they are, where they go?
I think a turkey came to feed
Searched around and found some seed
Oh, what funny little tracks in the snow

Oh, what funny little tracks in the snow
Don't you wonder what they are, where they go?
I think that it was a deer
It came very near
Oh, what funny little tracks in the snow

Oh, what funny little tracks in the snow
Don't you wonder what they are, where they go?
I think it was a cardinal red
With a crest upon it's head
Oh, what funny little tracks in the snow

Oh, what funny little tracks in the snow
Don't you wonder what they are, where they go?
I think that it was a sheep
Across the snow it did leap
Oh, what funny little tracks in the snow

Oh, what funny little tracks in the snow
Don't you wonder what they are, where they go?
I think that it was a horse
Trotted down the road of course
Oh, what funny little tracks in the snow

Oh, what funny little tracks in the snow
Don't you wonder what they are, where they go?
I think that it was a cow
I can hear it mooing now
Oh, what funny little tracks in the snow

Oh, what funny little tracks in the snow
Don't you wonder what they are, where they go?
I think that it was a chicken
For its gizzard stones was pickin'
Oh, what funny little tracks in the snow

The Ballad of The Goose
on Stetson Brook

Linda Heaton heard this story sometime in the past, traced it by a long distance phone call, and so became the oral history source for this project. Margaret and Linda and her first grade class took a field trip up Stetson Brook in Warren. The school at the bottom of the hill and the house at the top of the hill are gone, but they saw the house where the nine kids lived and tried to guess where the snow cave had formed by the bridge. With lists of rhyming words and a name for the goose, this ballad took form as if by magic. One of the girls made up the first part of the tune.

Warren

Geese are very cantankerous. They hiss, snap, and beat their strong wings at strangers. But geese are also very curious and make good pets. They often like to stick close to people and follow them around. Years ago many people kept geese because they needed feathers. When geese molt they shed a layer of feathers, just like a dog or cat sheds its fur. These feathers were used to fill feather ticks, which are bed-sized pillows. Back then people didn't have the kind of beds we have today. Rope was laced back-and-forth across the bed frame. This rope webbing was used to support a straw tick, and then a feather tick was put on top of that. Goose feathers were important for comfort and also for warmth. When farmers killed their geese, they would pluck all of the feathers, including the soft, fluffy down which geese don't shed. Down was used to fill cloth comforters. They were lightweight and very warm — just right for Vermont winters!

The Ballad of The Goose on Stetson Brook

Goos - ie Lu - cy fol - lowed me Down to school one day, I shooed her home but — still she roamed Though I told her to stay.

Goosie Lucy followed me
Down to school one day
I shooed her home but still she roamed
Though I told her to stay

It all began so long ago
This tale was told through sharing
Of a goose that lived on a hill in Warren
A goose strong-willed and daring

Tierney told this tale to Turner
Turner told it to Smithy
Smithy told it to Linda Heaton
Linda Heaton told it to me

One hundred years ago
It was in the fall
I went down to the neighbor's house
To those nine kids did call

Goosie Lucy followed me
Down to school one day
I shooed her home but still she roamed
Though I told her to stay

We crossed the bridge on Stetson Brook
We walked a mile morning and night
But to our sorrow when we got home
Our goose had taken flight

We looked for her both high and low
She could not be found
Winter came, the brook froze over
And heavy snows came down

We'd slide on our sleds, the snow did glisten
Then we'd walk to school
On quiet days on the bridge we'd listen
And hear the water below

Spring came, the days were warm
Snow melted, the brook was running
A snow cave opened by the bridge
Round and round Goosie was swimming

We picked her up and carried her home
Our parents were surprised
We sang and we danced and we jumped with joy
Our Goosie had survived

Goosie Lucy followed me
Down to school one day
I shooed her home but still she roamed
Though I told her to stay

James Wilson, Bradford Globe-Maker

It doesn't always take a lot of money or a fancy education to do something special. "Tinkering" is a longstanding Vermont tradition. And people who tinker often come up with some amazing inventions. A person with special skills and know-how starts working on a problem. Mix in a little inspiration and presto — you have an invention which does something new. In the 1830s Thomas Davenport, a Brandon blacksmith, was fascinated by electricity. He developed an electric motor. Samuel Morey of Fairlee invented a paddlewheel steamboat and also built an internal combustion engine. This kind of engine was later used in automobiles, but when he invented it in 1826 people weren't very interested. It took a while for the rest of the world to catch up. Tinkering is still going on today. But today it's computers, rather than machines, that now capture most tinkerers' imaginations.

Glenda Rose's third-grade class, of Bradford, read several local accounts of the remarkable achievements of this self-taught man. James Wilson lived beyond the school on Fairground Road.

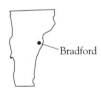

Bradford

James Wilson, Bradford Globe-Maker

Minor tune

When James Wilson was ten, He crept out at night to watch stars, He saw the Big and Little Dipper, the Big and Little Bear.

The world is round and so is a globe, Spin, spin, spin, James Wilson of Bradford made a globe, We sing to honor him.

When James Wilson was ten
He crept out at night to watch stars
He saw the Big and Little Dipper
The Big and Little Bear
The world is round and so is a globe
Spin, spin, spin
James Wilson of Bradford made a globe
We sing to honor him

He wondered about the seasons
What made day and night
All by himself knew the moving sun
Caused the dark and light
The world is round and so is a globe
Spin, spin, spin
James Wilson of Bradford made a globe
We sing to honor him

He grew up a blacksmith and farmer
Came to Bradford at age thirty-three
From his farm on Fairground Road
Said "Stars still come out for me"
The world is round and so is a globe
Spin, spin, spin
James Wilson of Bradford made a globe
We sing to honor him

"The world is round, round, round
And so is a globe"
He saw one in Hanover
Said "I could make one of those"
The world is round and so is a globe
Spin, spin, spin
James Wilson of Bradford made a globe
We sing to honor him

He made tools and a wooden ball
To learn engraving walked two hundred miles
From his blacksmith shop in eighteen-ten
Sold his first globe and smiled
The world is round and so is a globe
Spin, spin, spin
James Wilson of Bradford made a globe
We sing to honor him

General George J. Stannard

The stone monument honoring General Stannard is fairly close to the school in Georgia. Teri Ober's grade 6 students were interested in learning about the life of the man it honored. With Margaret they read John Duffy's Vermont, An Illustrated History for inspiration. All the quotes are from General George J. Stannard's battle report.

Vermonters have long prided themselves on being a free and independent people. Vermont has always been a land of small farms owned by individual farmers. There were no plantations here run on slave labor. Our state constitution outlawed slavery. In the years before the Civil War, feelings against slavery ran strong in the northern states, including Vermont. Abolitionist speakers argued strongly that slavery should be abolished, and they toured the state stirring up antislavery feelings. Vermonters formed an important link in the Underground Railway. They helped runaway slaves on the last leg of their long journey to freedom in Canada. It all had to be done in secret because it was against the law to help a slave who was running away. Some Vermonters even had secret rooms to hide slaves who were passing through. The conflict over slavery came to a head when the pro-slavery southern states decided to leave the Union. That was the beginning of the American Civil War. Vermont is a small state, but, for its size, Vermont sent many men to fight in the Civil War. Almost every Vermont town has a monument to soldiers who fought in the war. Many were killed in battle or by disease and never came home.

General George J. Stannard

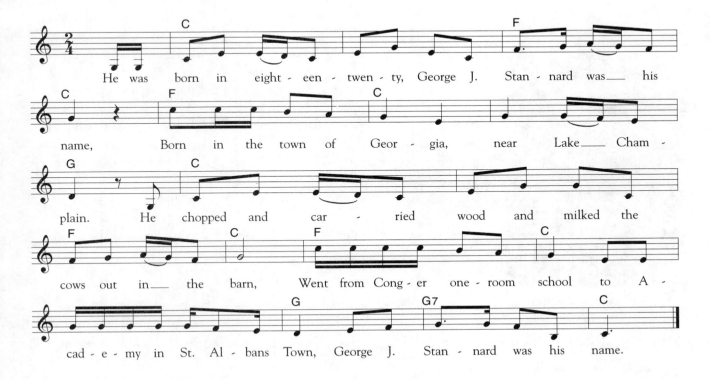

He was born in eight-een - twen-ty, George J. Stan-nard was___ his name, Born in the town of Geor-gia, near Lake___ Cham - plain. He chopped and car - ried wood and milked the cows out in___ the barn, Went from Cong-er one-room school to A - cad-e-my in St. Al-bans Town, George J. Stan-nard was his name.

He was born in eighteen-twenty, George J. Stannard was his name,
Born in the town of Georgia, near Lake Champlain
He chopped and carried wood and milked the cows out in the barn
Went from Conger one-room school to Academy in St. Albans Town
Geroge J. Stannard was his name

He commanded the St. Albans regiment at the start of the Civil War
He was the first Vermonter to volunteer
In Pennsylvania he was General of the Second Vermont Brigade
As Pickett charged in 'sixty-three, a flanking attack he made
George J. Stannard was his name

In an open field at Gettysburg under heavy fire of shell
These farmers, like veterans, like performing a battalion drill
With promptness and precision advanced in three flank attacks
His Vermonters at Gettysburg turned the Rebel Army back
George J. Stannard was his name

At a later battle in Richmond Stannard lost his arm
After the war he came back home and bought a farm
He died in eighteen-eighty-six, at his grave in Burlington
A bronze statue honors him, in Georgia a monument of stone
George J. Stannard was his name

Newbury's Bedell Bridge

These stories came from Katherine Blaisdell's Over the River and Through the Years *and from newspaper accounts of the wedding party. The song was created by Mary Hays' grade 4/5 in Newbury during their intensive study of the Connecticut River.*

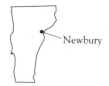

Newbury

In nineteenth century Vermont, farmers raised a variety of animals for sale in the Boston market. This was an important source of cash income. And in the era before truck transport, it was common practice to drive flocks of turkeys and geese, and herds of cattle and sheep on-foot all the way to the city. There's even an area in the town of Corinth called Goose Green because that's where farmers assembled their individual flocks for the long trip to the city. Joe Tuttle remembers his grandmother telling about his grandfather driving sheep and turkeys to Boston: "Two or three families would get together and rig up an old covered wagon. He'd be gone at least three weeks. He had to take all the groceries and horse feed, feed for the turkeys, sheep. They used to have corrals they put the sheep in at night. Generally the turkeys roosted in the trees. My grandmother said one night the turkeys roosted on somebody's old shed. They was so heavy it broke the shed down."

Newbury's Bedell Bridge

CHORUS **G** **C**

That old cov - ered bridge in New - bur - y, Made by Moo - dy Be - dell, Car - ried

Am **D** **G** *Fine*

teams and dro - vers and ped - lars In the years be - fore it fell.

VERSE **G** **Am**

Grand - pa pulled the rope to o - pen the toll house gate from the Ver - mont side, Pe -

D7 **G**

des - trians crossed for two cents, teams of hors - es or ox - en, five; The

C

first au - to a - cross the bridge, Doc - tor Rus - sell from Hav - er - hill, What to

Am **D** **G** *D.C.*

charge him? Twen - ty five cents af - ter we pushed him up the hill.

Chorus:
That old covered bridge in Newbury
Made by Moody Bedell
Carried teams and drovers and pedlars
In the years before it fell

Grandpa pulled the rope to open the toll house gate from the
    Vermont side
Pedestrians crossed for two cents, teams of horses or oxen, five
The first auto across the bridge, Doctor Russell from Haverhill
What to charge him? Twenty five cents after we pushed him up the
    hill

Chorus

Long ago there was no money in the town we live in now
We sent flocks and herds to Boston, of turkeys, geese, sheep and cows
To get turkeys into Boston, they had to travel far
So farmers spread upon their feet heavy coats of tar

Chorus

Across the Bedell Bridge a drover boy named Murphy
Drove on foot to Boston one hundred fifty turkeys
At farms along the Coos Turnpike many went astray
'Til he sprinkled corn and gathered many more along the way

Chorus

Pedlars with thread and needles and pins, iron kettles and molasses
Cups and dippers made of tin, salt and pepper and axes
They'd cross the bridge in their pungs or their little red carts
Weigh Mama's rags, barter and trade, then they would depart

Chorus

Like a huge barrel to flatten snow, through the bridge came the snow
    roller
It went rolling on but the man fell off, and he got rolled over
When he got up he left a print like a gingerbread man
His team and roller were rolling on, so after them he ran

Chorus

In nineteen-seventy-nine Richard and Winnifred[1] remember
The day before their wedding, the fourteenth of September
They were on the bridge where they would wed the very next day
But there came wind and lightning and the bridge it blew away

Chorus

---

[1] Richard and Winnifred Patten.

Central Vermont Railroad Tragedy

Margaret MacArthur learned this song from Natalie Bruce of Marlboro in the early 1960s.

In the 1800s there were no automobiles or airplanes, not even any highways. The railroad was the quickest and most convenient way to travel long distances. Unlike today, there were lots of passenger trains and they were almost always crowded with people. When a train had an accident it was a major disaster — like an airplane crash today. The Hartford train wreck occurred just north of White River Junction in February of 1887, on a night when it was 18 degrees below zero. It was big news and was reported even in the California papers. Four passenger cars fell from a high bridge to the frozen surface of the White River. Coal heating stoves and kerosene lanterns quickly set the wooden cars aflame. Henry Tewksbury of Randolph, a survivor of the crash, reported at the time: "I saw a young lady and gentleman who were apparently pinned down and could not extricate themselves. I saw the flames creeping nearer and nearer and heard them bid each other an affectionate good-by, and almost instantly they were enveloped by the cruel fire and I saw no more of them." Such vivid accounts made a deep impression on people and gave rise to a song. That song has been passed down to us today.

Central Vermont Railroad Tragedy

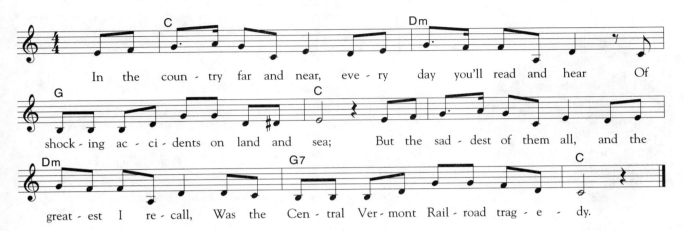

In the coun-try far and near, eve-ry day you'll read and hear Of shock-ing ac-ci-dents on land and sea; But the sad-dest of them all, and the great-est I re-call, Was the Cen-tral Ver-mont Rail-road trag-e-dy.

In the country far and near, every day you'll read and hear
Of shocking accidents on land and sea
Bur the saddest of them all, and the greatest I recall
Was the Central Vermont Railroad tragedy

'Twas the Montreal Express, it was speeding at its best
When at Hartford Bridge it struck a broken rail
Then with a fearful crash, to the river it was dashed
And a hundred souls went down to meet their fate

Horror met the victims gaze, as the wreck was soon ablaze
And fainting cries of help were sad to hear
None responded to the call, so they perished one and all
In the Central Vermont Railroad tragedy

There is one I'll not forget, that was little Joe Legret
He was with his father on that fatal night
He wasn't injured in the fall, but when he heard his father call
From the wreck he tried to save him, but in vain

"Alas my boy" said he, "there is no help for me"
As the flames around his head began to curl
Little Joe began to cry, when his father said "Good-bye
We'll meet again up in another world"

It was shocking to relate, it was sad to contemplate
No words can paint a picture of that sight
Little they thought that death was nigh, when they bid their
friends good-bye
When leaving home upon that fatal night

In the country far and near, every day you'll read and hear
Of shocking accidents on land and sea
But the saddest of them all and the greatest I recall
Was the Central Vermont Railroad tragedy

Weathersfield Panther

Most people agree that the last panther in Vermont was killed in Barnard in 1881, but some aren't so sure. Every year panther sightings are reported all around the state. In the town of Braintree, an elusive panther has become a local legend. There's even a granite statue of it at the Braintree Hill Meetinghouse. Panthers live in the deep forest. Like the deer on which they prey, panthers were forced out of their natural habitat as farmers cleared land for fields and pasture. Because they attacked domestic livestock, the early settlers hated panthers and hunted them to near extinction. Wild deer were brought back to Vermont and set free in the 1880s. We still don't know for sure whether the panthers have come back as well.

The children in Karen McGee's grade 2 in Perkinsville wanted to write about the stuffed panther in the Weathersfield Historical Society Museum. Using information from Edith Hunter's History of Weathersfield for Young People, Margaret and the students learned the story of this famous cat. After thinking about how the panther might have felt, studying photos of big cats, and making up long lists of relevant words, they wrote the song from the animal's point of view.

Perkinsville

Weathersfield Panther

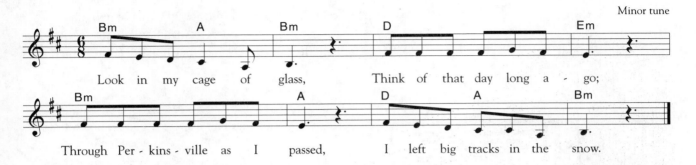

Look in my cage of glass, Think of that day long a - go;

Through Per - kins - ville as I passed, I left big tracks in the snow.

Look in my cage of glass
Think of that day long ago
Through Perkinsville as I passed
I left big tracks in the snow

With my sharp claws and long tail
Quiet, I sneaked through the town
Pounced on a rock and I saw
A cave where I could lie down

I spit and I snarled and I roared
When I awoke to a crash
In came Dewitt Gardner's dog
I sent that dog out fast

Dewitt Gardner looked in
Saw my eyes sparkle and gleam
Then he took his gun
Now I am only a dream

I was the Weathersfield Panther
I could run very fast
Now I stand in this cage
I am a thing of the past

Look in my cage of glass
Think of that day long ago
Through Perkinsville as I passed
I left big tracks in the snow

Green Mountain Renovator

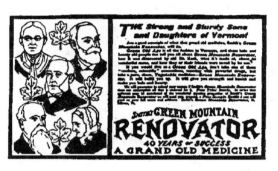

Medical researchers today are always trying to find new drugs to help treat diseases. When they find something which seems to work, it has to be carefully tested before it can be sold in drug stores. Sometimes it takes many years before a new drug is approved for sale. This wasn't always so. At the turn of the century anyone could patent their own secret medicinal brew and say whatever they liked about its benefits. Store shelves were lined with patent medicines claiming to cure just about any disease or condition. Today the names sound pretty exotic: "Dr. Kilmer's Swamp-Root," "Lydia Pinkham's Vegetable Compound," "H.E. Bucklen's Arnica Salve." Some of these remedies were based on herbal medicines that had been passed from generation to generation, and they may really have worked. Some traditional medicines have proven curative value and are still used today. But many patent medicines were hoaxes which someone put together only to make money. And many contained large percentages of alcohol. These sold well during times when liquor was forbidden.

Christine Cook's Grade 5 in Georgia interviewed Peter Mallett, local historian, in their schoolroom. In addition to telling them about Silas Smith and his concoction, he brought some of the old bottles, labels, and even the recipe. The Chorus "Green Mountain Renovator…." is a direct quote from the label. The input of several students who had dug in old bottle dumps gave a perfect introduction to use with the wealth of information given by Peter Mallett.

Georgia

Green Mountain Renovator

Once as I walked in the woods, along a path by an old foundation,
My hound saw a mound and dug in the ground, I saw a gleam in the sun
It was the rim of an amber bottle, mysterious to my mind
I picked up a stick and started to dig, and guess what I did find

I found an amber bottle all covered over with mud
I cleaned it in a nearby puddle, this is what it said:
"Green Mountain Renovator, It will build you up
It will give you strength and health, And make you hale and hearty"

I brought the bottle home "Grandma, look what I found"
She said "Oh yeah, I know about that, it was made in Georgiatown
Silas Smith he sent his kids in eighteen-fifty-four
To collect the herbs to make the brew they peddled door to door"

They dug gentian root, added senna leaves
Orange peel, potassium and hops, coriander and anise seeds
Then they poured the liquid in water and last of all
They added four gallons of full strength alchohol

"Green Mountain Renovator, It will build you up
It will give you strength and health, And make you hale and hearty"

One Room School in Marlboro

People sometimes say that in the "good old days" children got a better education. But they forget that, in the good old days, district schools were a lot wilder and the children more unruly. The big boys in the eighth grade might be eighteen years old because they only came to school when they weren't needed on the farm. The teacher, who often wasn't much older, could have a hard time making them behave. Sometimes the big boys would make a plan to "throw the teacher out." One of them would purposely get in trouble. When the teacher tried to punish him, they would gang up and carry the teacher out the door. When that happened in Braintree many years ago, Elijah Flint was the teacher and the big boy was Homer Young. As Perkins Flint remembers, "When Homer came after Elijah, Elijah caught him and he throwed him, and his head struck the side of the schoolhouse so hard that he dropped right down to the floor and he laid there. The rest of us all got in our seats by that time. And we was scared, we thought Homer was dead. After a little he begin to wiggle and twist, and quick as he got his bearings, he got back into his seat. And after that you could have heard a pin drop in that schoolhouse anytime that Elijah Flint said so."

The inspiration for this song came from interviews done by David Holtzapfel's Senior Room (5/6) students. They interviewed Jenny Dalrymple, who attended a one-room school in Marlboro and Alice Whitney, who taught in one. In many cases, we used their phrasing or words.
(See also Old Time Sugaring in Marlboro, *page 86.)*

Marlboro

One Room School in Marlboro

Have you ever seen a one room schoolhouse
With a little house out back?
Kids from six to sixteen one teacher taught
If you did something wrong you were caught
Every day we walked to school
Rain or shine, hot or cool
In the winter we wallered, in summer we walked
The girls wore dresses and the boys wore slacks
Somebody's living there today
In the schoolhouse where we used to play

If the water pail is empty walk half a mile to fill the pail
Each student had a tin cup hanging on a nail
Clean up your own mess, share a double desk
Don't be wasteful, turn your paper, use the rest
Although we went to school because we wanted to learn
And were taught to be ladies and gentlemen
Someone put a snake in the teacher's desk
But she just picked it up to show the rest
Somebody's living there today
In the schoolhouse where we used to play

We locked the teacher in the backhouse and she never told
When a boy stuffed the chimney, came down and said "It's cold"
He stoked up the fire 'til the room turned blue
Teacher sent us home early 'cause we all sneezed "achoo"
One nooning[2] we went out to play and teacher took a nap
I tiptoed in and the clock along I set
Teacher sent us home early that day
But my brother squealed at home, for a week I couldn't play
Somebody's living there today
In the schoolhouse where we used to play

At nooning the boys might go to the brook
With a piece of string, a stick and a hook
Sometimes when the fishing was great
It was too bad for them when they came home late
At nooning we went out to play
In Mather's mowing across the way
We stomped down the weeds to play ball
Where today there's no sign of a mowing at all
Somebody's living there today
In the schoolhouse where we used to play

---

[1] Wallowing through the snow.
[2] The noon hour.

The Ballad of Runaway Pond

Grade 8, Miller Run School, Sheffield, read Harry A. Phillips' History of Glover, Vermont and Runaway Pond — A Poem in Two Cantos. Phillips writes: "The first canto is the story of the draining of Long Pond as told by my great-grandmother, Janet Chamberlain Phillips, daughter of Spencer Chamberlain, the man who ran ahead of the stream." Margaret and the students condensed and rewrote a portion of the poem, using some phrases that might have come from eyewitness accounts of the 1810 disaster.

Sheffield

After the American Revolution, our new country's relationship with England was still uncertain. We fought England again during the War of 1812. One of the most important battles was fought on Lake Champlain in Plattsburgh Bay, right across from Burlington. At that time the English controlled Canada so the enemy was right next door. Vermonters felt that it was important to have some kind of defense just in case there was trouble, and every town had a local militia. The first Tuesday in June was the day fixed by law for the annual inspection and drill. The militia group was made up of local farmers and commanded by veterans from the earlier wars. At first it was probably like our National Guard Reserve, a group that trains seriously to be ready for trouble. But as time went along and the threat from the English lessened, the June training days became more like a day-long party. In the pages of Abby Hemenway's *Gazetteer*, a St. Albans observer remembers a June day long ago: "The village is soon alive with men and boys. The taverns, stores, and shops are full. The barkeepers in their shirt sleeves are doing a lively business, and the music of the toddy stick[1] is incessant."

---

[1] A toddy stick is used to stir a toddy, which is a drink of brandy, gin, whiskey or rum mixed with hot water, sugar and spices.

The Ballad of Runaway Pond

As I drive the back way to Burlington
Down by the old swamp by the road
Cat-tails and dead trees call back mem'ries
Long Pond legacy of long ago
Once Long Pond lay by Glover's south boundary
One hundred feet deep and a mile or so long
Surrounded by unbroken wilderness
Beech, birch, maple, hemlock, spruce and pine

There were no paths, no roads and no meadows
When Long Pond flowed south and into Horse Pond
Through Greensboro to the Lamoille River
Then on to Lake Champlain beyond
To the north lay Stone Pond and the grist mill
Aaron Wilson ground all sorts of grain
On this flouring mill families depended
The only one o'er all this town's domain

In eighteen hundred and ten, in the spring time
Streams were dry and Stone Pond was low
A drought prolonged there had been, when
The old mill wheel it would scarcely go.
The sixth day of June was Militia Day
Men gathered for their yearly drill
But the drought and hard cider and whiskey
Turned talk to power to run Wilson's Mill

"Though Long Pond it flows to the southward
We need water Stone Pond for to fill
We will dig a small trench to the northward
 For power to run Wilson's Mill"
Each Glover man took a pick-axe or shovel
To dig a small trench so the millwheel would go
But they broke through the Old Mother Earth dam
Runaway Pond, how the waters do roll

Continued on next page

The Ballad of Runaway Pond

Continued from previous page

From below comes a roaring like thunder
Each reddened face turns pale with fright
They see boiling and silvery quicksand
The water has gone from sight
Through the quicksand the waters now lower
Down the valley in madness to spill
O'er the deafening roar hear the men cry
"Wilson, where will you find your mill?"

(For this verse sing the last 8 measures of the tune.)
"My wife the corn is a-grinding
She knows nought of this terrible force
God in heaven, hear my prayer now
Will nothing stop this wild water's course"

An Indian by name Spencer Chamberlain
Age twenty-four and of stature grand
Born of a long line of runners
From New Hampshire, Westmoreland
He is off like a swift flying arrow
As a fifty foot wall of water does come
Carrying half-acres of tall standing timber
Hear the men cry "Run, Chamberlain, run"

Five long miles through the uncharted forest
Followed close by the water's wild roar
Nerves strained and as swift as an eagle
He gains the mill-house door
The woman stands frozen like marble
He sweeps her up and he leaps up the hill
As the waters tear off the old building
As the waters bear off the old mill

Through the valley the flood waters roaring
Toward Memphremagog, 'twill be their new home
To leave a swamp that we call Runaway Pond
And the legend of Spencer Chamberlain
When each Glover man took a pick axe or shovel
To dig a small trench so the mill wheel would go
But they broke through the Old Mother Earth dam
Runaway Pond, how the waters did roll

Looking Back on the 20th Century

Maple Sweet

For generations of Vermonters, sugaring has been a family affair, and kids have had important jobs to do. Lucien Whitehill remembers helping out as a boy, almost 90 years ago: "Father always bought us new rubber boots for sugaring. In them days you had wooden buckets. Kids was so much lighter than the men, we could walk on the crust and hold them. Father'd stay on the sled and hand us the buckets, and we'd take them and put them aside of the tree." Like the rest of farming, sugaring has changed a great deal over the years. Wooden buckets have been replaced by metal ones. They are much lighter and easier to handle. Some people don't use buckets at all and have converted to plastic pipeline. Years ago farmers gathered sap with a team of horses or oxen. Now most people use tractors. Mr. Whitehill remembers one man in his town who used to boil sap in an iron kettle. Now some people use a special machine which separates out most of the water so they don't have to boil so long. And today there are fewer people sugaring. As Mr. Whitehill observes, "When I was a kid there was 65 sugar places here in town and today I guess there's only five or six sugaring." One thing hasn't changed, though. During sugaring, there's still plenty of work to do and kids still help out.

Maple Sweet was written by Perrin Fisk, a 19th century Vermont poet. This is the song as Margaret MacArthur sings it.

Maple Sweet

VERSE
When you see the va-por pil-lar link the for-est and the sky,
Then you'll know the su-gar mak-ing sea-son's draw-ing nigh. Frost-y
nights and thaw-y days make the ma-ple pul-ses play 'Til con-
ges-ted with their sweet-ness they de-light to bleed a-way.

CHORUS
Then, bub-ble bub-ble bub-ble, bub-ble bub-ble goes the pan,
Fur-nish bet-ter mu-sic for the sea-son if you can. See the gold-en bil-lows,
watch their ebb and flow, Sweet-est joys in-deed we su-gar ma-kers know.

When you see the vapor pillar link the forest and the sky
Then you'll know the sugar making season's drawing nigh
Frosty nights and thawy days make the maple pulses play
'Til congested with their sweetness they delight to bleed away

Chorus:
Then, bubble bubble bubble, bubble bubble goes the pan
Furnish better music for the season if you can
See the golden billows, watch their ebb and flow
Sweetest joys indeed we sugar makers know

When you see the farmer trudging with his dripping buckets home
Then you'll know the sugar making season it has come
Fragrant odors pour through the open cabin door
The eager children rally ever crying loudly "more"

Chorus

You may wax it, you may grain it, fix it anyhow to eat
You'll always smack your lips and say "It's very, very sweet"
For the greenest leaves you see on the spreading maple tree
They sip and sip all summer and the autumn beauties be

Chorus

So you say you don't believe it, take a saucer and a spoon
Though you're sourer than a lemon, you'll be sweeter very soon
'Til every one you meet, at home or on the street
They'll have half a mind to bite you for you look so very sweet

Chorus

Memories of Old Craftsbury

Years ago kids on a farm had lots of responsibility. From the time they were born, they were with their Mother and Father as they worked in the barn, house, or field. Children started out with small jobs and, as they got older, assumed more and more responsibility. They often helped care for calves and young stock, brought cows to and from pasture, and helped "slop down" the cattle at milking time. Everyone, of course, helped with haying! Every member of the family had a job to do, and each job was important and helped the family earn a living. Families today are not as self-sufficient as they once were. Farm kids still have chores to do before and after school. But there are fewer farms, and most children no longer have as much opportunity to help their family earn a living and learn valuable skills from their parents. Jean Conklin speaks for many older farmers when she laments, "Now you see so many boys and girls with so much time on their hands. And nothing that really has to be done by them. I think that it's sad that they can't feel the importance of being needed, in an economic sense."

Judy Locke's Grade 5, in Craftsbury, created this song from oral history interviews. Except for line three, the chorus is a quote from one of the student's interviews with a town elder. The morning dew, spider webs, and calling "bob-ee-links" speak poetically of life on the Vermont farm.

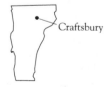

Craftsbury

Memories of Old Craftsbury

Minor tune

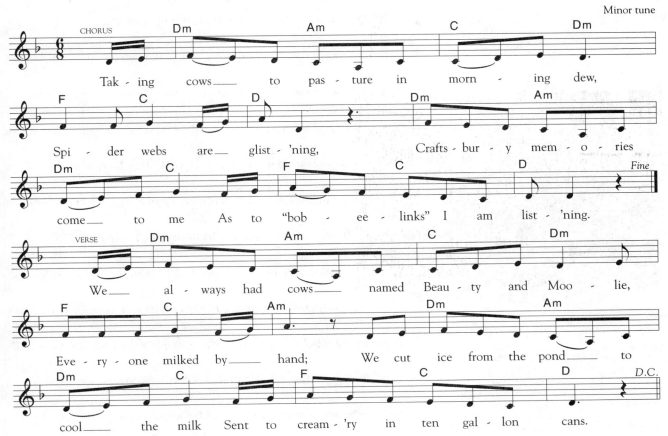

Chorus:
Taking cows to pasture in morning dew
Spider webs are glist'ning
Craftsbury memories come to me
As to "bo-bee-links" I am list'ning

We always had cows named Beauty and Moolie
Everyone milked by hand
We cut ice from the pond to cool the milk
Sent to cream'ry in ten gallon cans

Chorus

Wayne's horse Kitty carried him to school
Then he'd point toward home and she'd go
Mary's father carried her to school draped in sleigh bells
That rang as they came through deep snow

Chorus

Hugh woke one morning to see Buck, an ox
That had wandered far from town
He made a bridle, climbed on Buck's back
Bound for school took the ox back home

Chorus

Bunny's up at four, then he sees the dawn
Rowing to check his trap line
On Little Hosmer Pond, mink or muskrat for cash
Back home ready for school by nine

Chorus

We made our own fun, a forty foot circle
In snow to play fox and geese
We had sugar parties, sugar on snow
Coffee, doughnuts, sour pickles to eat

Chorus

Grandmas and Grandpas of Swanton

Today's grandmas and grandpas grew up in an era when people in rural Vermont didn't have very much money. They lived on small farms. They raised cows, pigs, and chickens, they sugared, they had a big garden, and canned and pickled their food. As the old-timers like to say, "They got their living from the farm." They were able to grow most of what they needed, and they didn't have as many things as people have today. At Christmas children were content with just one gift. Oranges were rare and something really special. It was a treat to find one in your stocking. Even store-bought candy was a luxury, although kids could have homemade maple sugar cakes whenever they liked. Instead of playing with expensive store-bought toys, children played games together, explored the woods, went fishing, or enjoyed home-made toys, dolls, whistles, tops, or kites created by their parents or grandparents. Older people, who grew up in these very different times, often remark that children today don't seem to know how to have fun without spending money.

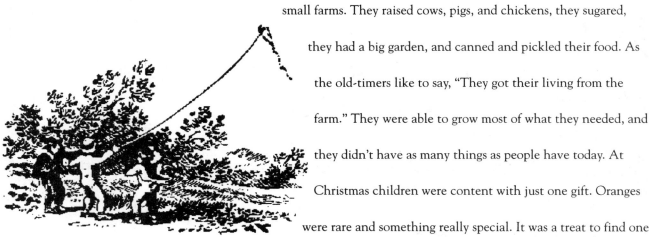

Marilyn Bish and Linda Peoro encouraged their grade 5 students to ask their grandparents about what they did for fun as youngsters. From these tape-recorded interviews, Margaret and the students made this song, often using direct quotes. The grandparents invariably said, "It was so much fun," and the class noticed that all of the fun was free.

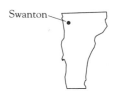

Swanton

Grandmas and Grandpas of Swanton

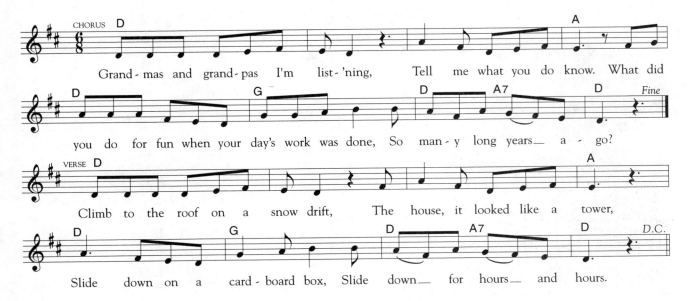

CHORUS
Grand-mas and grand-pas I'm list-'ning, Tell me what you do know. What did
you do for fun when your day's work was done, So man-y long years a-go?

VERSE
Climb to the roof on a snow drift, The house, it looked like a tower,
Slide down on a card-board box, Slide down for hours and hours.

Chorus:
Grandmas and grandpas I'm list'ning
Tell me what you do know
What did you do for fun when your day's work was done
So many long years ago?

Climb to the roof on a snowdrift
The house, it looked like a tower
Slide down on a cardboard box
Slide down for hours and hours

Toggle up a toboggan
Wood and old barrel staves
Exciting for kids and lots of fun
'Cause it was something you made

A helmet homemade from a water tank
For diving in Lake Champlain
Cardboard piano boxes for ice fishing shanties
To keep out the snow, wind, and rain

Chorus

Too much yeast in homemade root beer
Would pop the top like a gun
Penny candy prizes for bingo and lotto
It was lots of fun when I won

Vanilla, eggs, cream and sugar
In a pail lined with tin
In a big wooden bucket of ice and salt
Gather 'round, give it a spin

Paper baskets for flowers on May Day
To hang on a neighbor's door
Popcorn strings at Christmas
Around the tree they go

Chorus

Build a little log cabin
The wood we'd chop and saw
To prove we were tough in wintertime
Go barefoot to barn in the snow

In the barn we would square dance
Girls curtsy, boys bow
For music we had a fiddler
And Vera played piano

Chorus

Old Time Sugaring in Marlboro

On Vermont farms in the early 1900s, white sugar was a luxury. It was made from sugar cane in warm climates far away, and you had to have money in order to buy it. Money, of course, was always in short supply. So Vermonters made their own sugar using the resources they had on hand. As Elmer Page remembers, "You used to cook your maple syrup down until it was real hard. Then you'd stir it down at the sugar house. You'd have two brand new hoes, just the same as your garden hoes. And two people would stand there and stir the sugar till it would get hard and lumpy, and keep stirring it until the lumps started breaking up. It would be just about like this brown sugar you buy now, maybe a little coarser. And they cooked with that. We had great big 32-gallon barrels in the pantry. And my grand-mother kept stirred-off maple sugar in one and flour in the other."

Jenny Dalrymple is called Aunt Rhody by her nieces and nephews, her middle name being Rhoda. Alice Whitney has many grandchildren in the school in Marlboro. Each of them was interviewed at home by a couple of students. From tapes of these oral histories Margaret and David Holtzapfel's Senior Room (5/6) students made this song. They found that sugaring has changed in Marlboro, with syrup now being put up in tins rather than being cooked down to sugar to prevent spoilage, and for ease of shipping. Dalrymple's sugar went east to Brattleboro, Whitney's from Higley Hill, went west to Wilmington. Both were wrapped in pretty papers the kids had pinked, and packed in handmade boxes. Alice's words make up the second half of the chorus. (See also One Room Schoolhouse in Marlboro, *page 74.)*

Marlboro

Old Time Sugaring in Marlboro

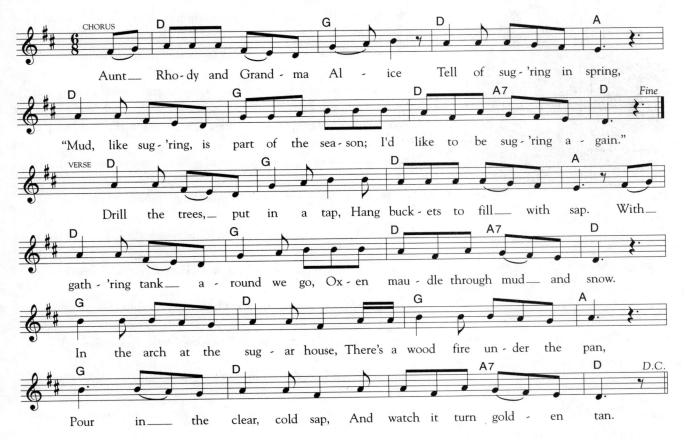

CHORUS
Aunt Rho-dy and Grand-ma Al-ice Tell of sug-'ring in spring,
"Mud, like sug-'ring, is part of the sea-son; I'd like to be sug-'ring a-gain."
VERSE
Drill the trees,— put in a tap, Hang buck-ets to fill— with sap. With—
gath-'ring tank— a-round we go, Ox-en mau-dle through mud— and snow.
In the arch at the sug-ar house, There's a wood fire un-der the pan,
Pour in— the clear, cold sap, And watch it turn gold-en tan.

Chorus:
Aunt Rhody and Grandma Alice
Tell of sug'ring in spring
"Mud, like sug'ring, is part of the season
I'd like to be sug'ring again"

Drill the trees, put in a tap,
Hang buckets to fill with sap.
With gathering tank around we go,
Oxen maudle[1] through mud and snow
In the arch at the sugar house
There's a wood fire under the pan
Pour in the clear, cold sap
And watch it turn golden tan

Chorus

Forty gallons of sap one of syrup makes
To eleven pounds it does boil
Then to the house to mold sugar cakes
Boil to eight pounds so they won't spoil
We packaged the cakes in papers we pinked,
Then we wrapped them airtight
All packed in layers in homemade crates
That Father to train would take

Chorus

At one in the morning fathers woke from dozin'
To leave with the teams while the roads were still frozen
In Brattleboro Dalrymple unloaded crates
To ship to Boston on the freight
From Higley Hill Wilmington way was best
Whitney's team pulled their sugar west
To go on the narrow gauge 'cross the trestle
That train called the Hoot Toot and Whistle

Chorus

---

[1] Trudge. A descriptive word of Jenny's.

Rozie Brown's Store

Meeting in an old schoolhouse adjacent to the Williston Central School in November, 1990, Margaret and a group of multi-aged students studied a video of a Williston Historical Society meeting where elders spoke of the town as it was in their childhood. This song came from these reminiscences, using many direct quotes. North Williston was a thriving community earlier in this century, with the store, a railroad station, an ingenious pre-electricity freezing plant, and many dairy farms that supplied milk to the cities. Fortunately for the kids, these memories remain, for the train no longer stops and the "character of the town has changed from rural and farming to mainly suburban and industrial", according to local historian Richard Allen, director of the song writing project and historical society member.

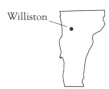

Williston

Every village used to have its general store. Travel by horse and buggy was slow and difficult. People couldn't drive long distances to get what they needed. The general store was nearby and had everything: flour, molasses, dried fish, patent medicine, cloth, boots, nails, stove pipe, and kerosene. As they used to say, "You name it. We have it. All we have to do is find it." There were benches on the front porch where older men watched the world go by. And there were chairs around the potbellied stove. Here men played checkers, smoked, and told stories and jokes late into the night. There was always a spittoon nearby because chewing tobacco was popular. If someone's aim wasn't good, the floor was a mess. In the days before rural free delivery, the post office was usually in the store. Women brought their eggs to trade for store-bought goods. And if their parents could afford it, children got a penny candy treat. The store was the center of the community.

Rozie Brown's Store

CHORUS
First came the rail-road, Then came the de-pot,
Then came the gen-'ral store, Gath-'ring place for the peo-ple.

VERSE
Roz-ie Brown's store had eve-ry-thing and more That an-y-bod-y could need,
Fish-ing pole, hook line and sink-er, Pins and nee-dles and thread,
Horse col-lars, straw hats and clothes, Bar-rels of pick-les and fish,
Cook-ies, crack-ers, pump your own mo-las-ses, You can get an-y-thing you wish.

Chorus:
First came the railroad, then came the depot
Then came the gen'ral store, gath'ring place for the people

Rozie Brown's store had everything and more
That anybody could need
Fishing pole, hook, line, and sinker
Pins and needles and thread
Horse collars, straw hats, and clothes
Barrels of pickles and fish
Cookies, crackers, pump your own molasses
You can get anything you wish

Chorus

The farmer's big hands would roll the milk cans
Onto the train to Boston
Then drive their teams back to the store
For gabbin' and for talkin'
Telephone exchange didn't cost any change
You could help plug in the wire
Sort the mail, put it in a big bag
Hook it to the fast train "Flyer"

Chorus

First freezing plant in all the land
Was by the store and the railroad track
When the cove was frozen men would go out knowin'
Time to cut the Chapman Cove ice
From here you could see all the geese that would flee
'Til all the hill looked white
A boy drove geese to the freezing plant
A boy in command all right

Chorus

We saw the bridge go down by ice coming up
In nineteen-twenty-three
It floated on down the Winooski River
Pushed by a big elm tree
To slide down Depot Hill was a great big thrill
All the way to the railroad track
After a chill or a winter spill
We'd go to Rozie Brown's before headin' back

Chorus

(Optional: repeat first verse.)

Last Saw Log Drive on the Connecticut

Margaret and Trudy Fadden's grade 4/5 from Newbury interviewed Katherine Blaisdell and read excerpts from her Over the River and Through the Years. *Then they read from Robert Pike's* Tall Trees, Tough Men *and made phone calls to Pittsburg to find the names of the Connecticut Lakes. They also viewed tools brought in by students and faculty members. They then wrote their song from a child's point of view.*

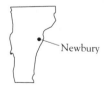
Newbury

In the early 1900s logging was very different than it is today. There were no chain saws, skidders, or log trucks, and all of the work was done by hand. It took two men on opposite ends of a crosscut saw to fell a tree. Logs were skidded out of the forest using horses or oxen. Logging was done in the winter when there was snow on the ground. The all-male crews lived together in logging camps far from their homes and families. Throughout the winter, logs were piled up along the river banks. When the spring melt came and the rivers rose, the logs would be dumped into the water and carried by the current to mills downstream. Some forest areas were distant from the broad, fast waters of the Connecticut River but were near smaller tributary streams. In this case, loggers would build a temporary dam to make a small pond. They would roll in as many logs as they could and when it was full, they would quickly yank out the dam. The sudden rush of water would carry the logs forward to deeper, faster waters farther downstream. These dams were called "flush dams."

Last Saw Log Drive on the Connecticut

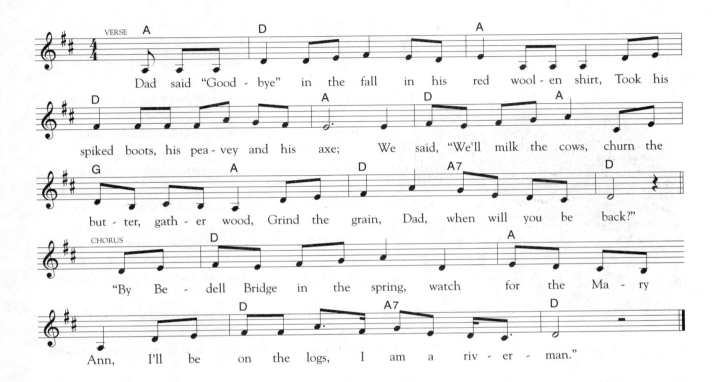

VERSE
Dad said "Good-bye" in the fall in his red wool-en shirt, Took his spiked boots, his pea-vey and his axe; We said, "We'll milk the cows, churn the but-ter, gath-er wood, Grind the grain, Dad, when will you be back?"

CHORUS
"By Be-dell Bridge in the spring, watch for the Ma-ry Ann, I'll be on the logs, I am a riv-er-man."

Dad said "Goodbye" in the fall in his red woolen shirt
Took his spiked boots, his peavey and his axe
We said, "We'll milk the cows, churn the butter, gather wood
Grind the grain, Dad, when will you be back?"
"By Bedell Bridge in the spring, watch for the Mary Ann
I'll be on the logs, I am a riverman"

From Lake Connecticut, Lake Camel, Lake Sophie near Pittsburg
Sixty five million feet of logs
When the ice broke in the spring of nineteen hundred fifteen
It was the last great drive with peaveys[1] and cant dogs[1]
"By Bedell Bridge in the spring, watch for the Mary Ann
I'll be on the logs, I am a riverman"

One fateful day at The Horse Race at Fifteen Mile Falls
From a rock they heard old drunk Sam's calls
Boss said, "Ten dollars to the man who can rescue old drunk Sam"
Dad rode a log down and grabbed Sam from the falls
"By Bedell Bridge in the spring, watch for the Mary Ann
I'll be on the logs, I am a riverman"

Jump for joy, run to the beanhole, dig it out, build a fire
In use for fifty years but never again
When the beanhole is good and hot, Bullard[2] will plant the iron pot
Then give us big ginger cookies at the Mary Ann[3]
"By Bedell Bridge in the spring, watch for the Mary Ann
I'll be on the logs, I am a riverman"

Coming 'round the Ox Bow and Bailey's Eddy
We can hear the logs bumping together
Then we see our dad with a mustache and a beard
Jumping from log to log light as a feather
"By Bedell Bridge in the spring, watch for the Mary Ann
I'll be on the logs, I am a riverman"

Dad jumped off the logs, came to the Mary Ann
"Have you kids been good while I've been gone
I'll be back to plow and sow, but now I have to go
To finish this last log drive to Mt. Tom."
"By Bedell Bridge in the spring, watch for the Mary Ann
I'll be on the logs, I am a riverman"

---

[1] Tools for rolling logs.
[2] Joe Bullard was one of the cooks on the river.
[3] The Mary Ann is a kitchen on a floating raft, also called a wanigan.

Pedlars from Pownal

The students in Gary Lamoureaux' grade 4 in Pownal gathered stories about their town through oral history interviews with town elders. This song was written from this research and includes memories from Fran Lampman, Mrs. McIver, Helen Renner, and Selma and Parley Palmer.

Pownal

Years ago many people used to peddle things door-to-door. Farmers could make more money selling butter directly to people in the village than they could trading it for goods and credit at the store. A farmer would work all week churning, salting, shaping, and wrapping up a good supply of butter. On Saturday he would hitch up his horse and drive to the village to deliver butter to his regular customers. Some farmers had butter routes, some had egg routes, some had milk routes — whatever a farmer could produce he could peddle. Peddlers also used to come to the farmers. Peddlers had a "territory" and came to the farm at regular intervals. Jewish peddlers traveled the back roads on foot, selling needles and thread from a pack on their back, while tin peddlers traded rags for tin pots and pans, which they carried in their carts. They brought useful goods and lots of news. Their arrival was a special event.

Pedlars from Pownal

Pedlars from Pownal, that peddling town
Hard working, hard fighting, contentious

Kids picked up chestnuts to sell
To buy their shoes in the fall
Carry shoes, go barefoot to church
Tough feet, shoes hardly worn at all

Pedlars from Pownal, that peddling town
Hard working, hard fighting, contentious

"Barefoot the minute there's no snow on Greylock"[1]
"Use it up, wear it out, make it do, do without"
Mending and reading by oil lamp light
We made our way without a doubt

Pedlars from Pownal, that peddling town
Hard working, hard fighting, contentious

Take horse and cart to Williamstown
Sell berries, squash, and potatoes
Smoked hams, chicken, butter, and cheese
Maple syrup, firewood, tomatoes

Pedlars from Pownal, that peddling town
Hard working, hard fighting, contentious

From Pawlet to Pownal to Charlemont[2]
Parley drove three hundred cattle down
Three week drives three times a year
Trading cows in every town

Pedlars from Pownal, that peddling town
Hard working, hard fighting, contentious

-----

[1] Quote from Helen Renner.
[2] In Massachusetts.

Weybridge Kids in the Old Days

Lunch hour at the district school used to be just that — an hour for lunch. And during that hour, children were free to do whatever they liked. Many brought their lunches in an old lard pail or went home for "dinner" if they lived nearby. After lunch, children played games like ball, hide 'n' seek, jump rope, or marbles, just like kids do today.

Katharine DuClos of Braintree remembers having noon-time fun: "In the winter we took our sleds and we could slide prit (*sic*) near home down that big hill, if it was good sliding. At noon, of course, we had an hour's nooning. We'd go out and slide down the hill. We'd go so far, we didn't get back in time. We kind of planned that."

These stories came from the memories of town elders through interviews conducted by the Grade 5/6 students with enthusiastic support from their teacher, Helen Freismuth.

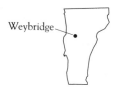

Weybridge

Weybridge Kids in the Old Days

O-ver the hill by the Lem-on Fair, One teach-er in a school made of stone; Be-cause all_ eight grades_ were in one room, Help-ing the young kids was fun. La-ter on came the aw-ful day when our School-house stones_ were car-ried a-way, They were laid in the road_ on Thomp-son Hill, To build it high-er; they're lay-ing there still, To build it high-er; they're lay-ing there still.

Over the hill by the Lemon Fair
One teacher in a school made of stone
Because all eight grades were in one room
Helping the young kids was fun
Later on came the awful day when our
Schoolhouse stones were carried away
They were laid in the road on Thompson Hill
To build it higher, they're laying there still
To build it higher, they're laying there still

We'd take our lunch and skates in winter
And head for the Lemon Fair
All of us for our whole lunch hour
Would skate round and round out there
We made angels in the snow
That sparkled like crystal in sun
We took our toboggans and our sleds
Down Joe Brown's hill for fun
Down Joe Brown's hill for fun

When after school I took milk in a bowl
To Aunt Sylvia Drake
She expected me curtsy
And stand perfectly straight
Then in the bowl she'd send home a cookie
But one day instead came a note
Your naughty daughter rolled down the hill
I saw her petticoat
I saw her petticoat

We hitched a ride to school with the milkman
Helped deliver milk on the way
After school changed clothes to wash the bottles
And do chores instead of play
When April showers brought May flowers
Who could find the most kind of posies?
And a fun game we used to play
Was Pom-pom-pull-away
Was Pom-pom-pull-away

To and Fro in Fairlee

Margaret worked with the students in the Fairlee Elementary Grade 5 to come up with this song. Robinson's History of Fairlee *gave them their ideas for these verses on transportation.*

Fairlee

At the turn of the century there were no paved roads in Vermont. Even gravel roads were scarce. Most roads were dirt, and the spring mud was unbelievably deep. Sometimes the roads were so bad that no one could go anywhere except on foot. Each town was responsible for maintaining its own roads. Farmers could work out part of their taxes by sending a hired man or a team to work on the road crew. Road work was usually done during times when people weren't very busy on the farm. But the roads often needed attention at other times of the year. A main road that went through several towns might be well tended in one town and almost impassable in another. As automobiles became more important, people expected to be able to travel farther. So the state government took responsibility for the main roads in order to make sure they were well-maintained everywhere. Edgar Butterfield remembers a car trip he took with his grandfather in a 1916 Model T Ford: "He picked me up when we lived in Sherburne, and I went with him up to my uncle's in Hyde Park. I remember hearing Grampa brag about how it was only something like eight hours making the trip. And we only had four flat tires. So that was what it was like to travel back in those days."

To and Fro in Fairlee

Minor tune

In seventeen-seventy-five, permission was granted to Israel Morey
To build to cross the Connecticut "A proper boat, a Publick Ferry"
Move along, to and fro
To ferry horses and wagons, children, women and men
From Orford to Fairlee Meadows, then carry goods back again
Back and forth the people go

Israel's son, Samuel Morey, made an engine powered by steam
To chug around the pond and the river in a steam boat was his dream
Move along, to and fro
Seventeen-ninety-three on the Connecticut during Sunday meeting hour
Boys were amazed at his speed in the first boat run by steam power
Back and forth the people go

Sixty years later a covered bridge connected Orford and Fairlee
Hold your breath, make a wish as you go in, come out the other side merrily
Move along, to and fro,
Our bridge, beloved for eighty years, retired old and worn
In nineteen-thirty-eight with arches we built a new bridge of iron
Back and forth the people go

In eighteen-forty-eight, with a funnel shaped smoke stack
Came "Green Mountain Boy" engine whistling down the track
Move along, to and fro
"Allie" Adams and his oxen hauled a thousand cords of wood to fire up the boiler of the train
On Connecticut and Passumpsic Line, today it's the Boston and Maine
Back and forth the people go

Now we have a thruway south to north, to Canada it goes
I-91 traffic moves fast, even in the winter snows
Move along, to and fro
With our ferry boats, steam boats and bridges, trains and highways too
Here in our town of Fairlee, back and forth the people go
Back and forth the people go

Shaftsbury Game Song

*These interesting anecdotes came from Fran Andres'
grade 6 students interviews with Ed Colvin
and Merton Snow. Kathy Link, Shaftsbury Arts
and Basics Program Director, arranged
and videotaped the interviews. Kathy's foresight
and enthusiasm in this successful pilot project
sparked Margaret's involvement in further
residencies throughout Vermont.*

Shaftsbury

Kids still go to the movies, but they're nowhere near as important today as they were earlier in this century. In the days before video, television, and even radio, the movies were exciting — and cheap. Every village of any size had some kind of theatre. City theatres were huge, fancy buildings with an enormous screen. Kids who didn't have to work on the farm crowded the Saturday matinees. And they came and went on their own. Moms and dads didn't drive them around. In addition to the film, there were newsreels and cartoons. Sometimes there was even a double feature. After the movie some kids might hang out at the local soda fountain or candy kitchen. They'd have a cherry coke or an ice cream soda and see who else was there. Even your grandparents were young once!

Shaftsbury Game Song

Traditional tune

CHORUS
What-'ll we do in Shafts-bur-y, in Shafts-bur-y, in Shafts-bur-y?
What-'ll we do in Shafts-bur-y on a Sat-ur-day af-ter-noon?

VERSE
We can go to Ben-ning-ton, to Ben-ning-ton, to Ben-ning-ton, For a
nick-el we can see the mov-ie and get a lol-li-pop. We can play
hide and seek with my bil-ly goat, he can count to six. Or
hitch him to the cart, he'll fol-low a crack-er tied in front of his nose to a stick.

What'll we do in Shaftsbury, in Shaftsbury, in Shaftsbury?
What'll we do in Shaftsbury on a Saturday afternoon?

We can go to Bennington, to Bennington, to Bennington
For a nickel we can see the movie and get a lollipop
We can play hide and seek with my billy goat, he can count
    to six
Or hitch him to the cart, he'll follow a cracker tied in front of
    his nose to a stick

What'll we do in Shaftsbury, in Shaftsbury, in Shaftsbury?
What'll we do in Shaftsbury on a Saturday afternoon?

We can tie a string to a pocket book and fill it with play money
Put it on the road, when someone stops, pull the string, it would
    be funny
We can play nipsie[1], we can carve the sticks
Or take an old wagon wheel, push it around with a stick

What'll we do in Shaftsbury, in Shaftsbury, in Shaftsbury?
What'll we do in Shaftsbury on a Saturday afternoon?

We can play jacks, we can play marbles in a ring
With our crystal alleys and our old clay marbles and we will
    shoot to win
Shoot golden rod arrows into the nest of a hornet
When they come at us, take radical flight

What'll we do in Shaftsbury, in Shaftsbury, in Shaftsbury?
What'll we do in Shaftsbury on a Saturday afternoon?

In winter on our jack jumper[2], down the hill we'll ride
Or on our two feet, on the crust we'll slide
Saturday is bathtime, take down the old washtub
On the stove heat the water, jump in the tub and rub-a-dub-dub
    scrub scrub

What'll we do in Shaftsbury, in Shaftsbury, in Shaftsbury?
What'll we do in Shaftsbury on a Saturday afternoon?

---

[1] An old time game.
[2] A ski-like plaything for sliding down hills. It had an elevated
seat installed on a wide board.

The Boston Girls
and the Long Trail Porcupine

When the railroad arrived in the 1840s, it connected Vermont with the big cities of the east coast — and the millions of people who lived there. Later in the century, down-country visitors flocked to grand hotels at mineral springs for a cure and relaxation. Others came to mountain resorts to escape the summer heat. Summer visitors became an important source of income for the state. Early in this century people began to be interested in something that they had always taken for granted — the beauty of the natural world. Camping and hiking became popular forms of recreation. People began to see wilderness areas as an important resource, which should be protected and accessible to the public for all time. Today we can visit and enjoy state parks and the national forest, or go for a hike on the Long Trail. We have our ancestors to thank for realizing the future value of these beautiful natural resources.

This true story comes from Jane and Will Curtis'
Green Mountain Adventure, Vermont's Long Trail.
Margaret and Patrice Miller's Grade 6, Derby, used
the old song Cripple Creek as a model for the chorus
and the tune, added some trappings and imaginings,
made a beginning, middle, and end, and came up with
a story in song, a proper ballad.

Derby

The Boston Girls and the Long Trail Porcupine

Tune: Cripple Creek

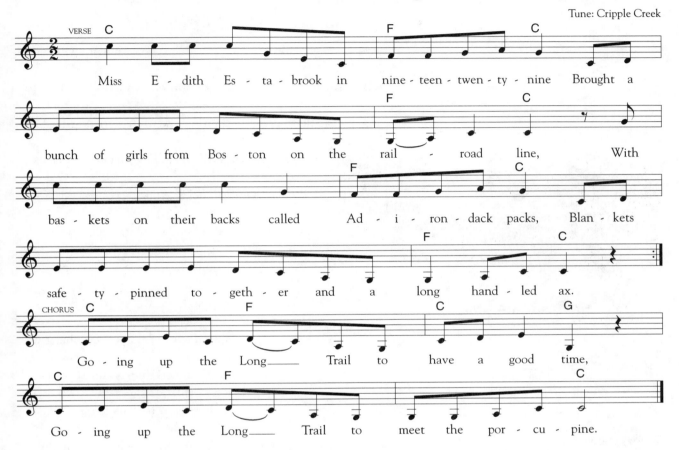

VERSE
Miss E - dith Es - ta - brook in nine - teen - twen - ty - nine Brought a
bunch of girls from Bos - ton on the rail - road line, With
bas - kets on their backs called Ad - i - ron - dack packs, Blan - kets
safe - ty - pinned to - geth - er and a long hand - led ax.

CHORUS
Go - ing up the Long___ Trail to have a good time,
Go - ing up the Long___ Trail to meet the por - cu - pine.

Miss Edith Estabrook in nineteen-twenty-nine
Brought a bunch of girls from Boston on the railroad line
With baskets on their backs called Adirondack packs
Blankets safety-pinned together and a long handled ax
A tin plate, a tin cup, a big old cooking pot
The girls got tired 'cause they carried a lot
They crawled into their bedrolls and went right to sleep
They crawled into their bedrolls and never made a peep

Chorus:
Going up the Long Trail to have a good time
Going up the Long Trail to meet the porcupine

Hours later they woke in a fright
They heard an "ominous gnawing" in the middle of the night
These mountains are three hundred fifty million years old
They're moaning and groaning and I can't be bold
"Miss Edith Estabrook, will you come quick
We hear a terrible noise and it is making us sick"
Miss Edith Estabrook said, "What can it be?"
She lit her carbide lantern so they could see

Chorus

They saw a lump of a beast all covered with spikes
Not what they expected to see on their hike
"What will we do?" "Get the guide book from the pack"
"It says knock him on the nose with the back of the ax"
They did just that and the ax worked fine
They boiled the beast in the pot 'til they were ready to dine
Miss Edith Estabrook said, "It tastes like calf's liver"
Some of the girls began to shake and to shiver

Chorus

They went back to Boston with their toothpick quills
They told the story of their Long Trail thrills
Going up the Long Trail to have a good time
Going up the Long Trail to eat the porcupine

The Moose and the Cow in Parker's Gore

The Abenaki lived in the area that is now Vermont without changing it very much. Their way of life was well adapted to the wilderness. But when the white settlers arrived, the land was surveyed and individual farmers began felling trees to clear fields. At first wool was the most important crop. All around the state, more and more land was cleared to pasture sheep. In 1840 Vermont looked very different than it does today — almost three quarters of the land was open. But times changed and wool was no longer profitable. As farmers shifted from sheep to dairy cattle, they let some of the pasture grow back up to trees. Over the years more land has returned to forest. Today only one quarter of the state is open. As the forest has returned to Vermont, so have the wild animals. Moose are now more common than at any time since the first white settlers arrived.

Song of the Wilderness is the title the students in Shayne Lylis' Grade 4 at the Sherburne School gave this work. Many of them had seen the moose on Carrera's farm, over the mountain from Sherburne. There was a book written on the subject and extensive news coverage of it. With guidance from Margaret and their teacher, they researched the Native American, Pe-al (two syllables), for whom the pond was named.

Sherburne

The Moose and the Cow in Parker's Gore

Mixolydian tune

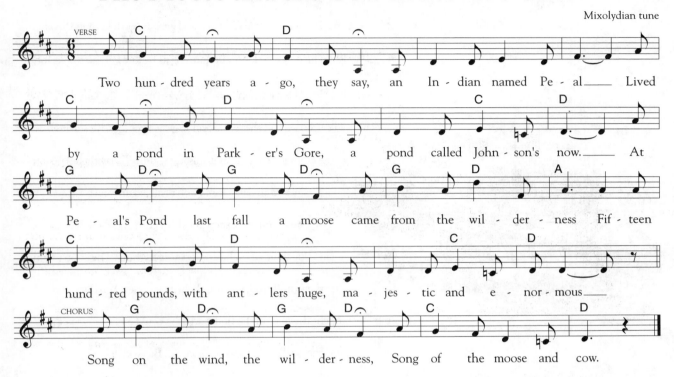

Two hun-dred years a-go, they say, an In-dian named Pe-al___ Lived by a pond in Park-er's Gore, a pond called John-son's now.___ At Pe-al's Pond last fall a moose came from the wil-der-ness Fif-teen hund-red pounds, with ant-lers huge, ma-jes-tic and e-nor-mous___

CHORUS Song on the wind, the wil-der-ness, Song of the moose and cow.

Two hundred years ago, they say, an Indian named Peal
Lived by a pond in Parker's Gore, a pond called Johnson's now
At Peal's Pond last fall a moose came from the wilderness
Fifteen hundred pounds, with antlers huge, majestic and
     enormous
Song on the wind, the wilderness
Song of the moose and the cow

Through the forest, through the stream this handsome beast he
     browsed
The whistling wind it called to him until he reached some cows
At the Carrera's farm one cold October day
Larry and Lila spied his horns as they fed their cattle hay
Song on the wind, the wilderness
Song of the moose and the cow

The herd of cattle moved away save for one friendly heifer
The bull moose strode up to her side and gently he
     caressed her
He lingered there by Jessica through two moons or more
They nuzzled and they chewed their cuds, content in Parker's
     Gore
Song on the wind, the wilderness
Song of the moose and the cow

The moose he stayed by Jessica, with love and dignity
Larry and Lila protected him, they lived in harmony
A most rare relationship, he stayed through the season
Though many hundreds came to see, none could know the
     reason
Song on the wind, the wilderness
Song of the moose and the cow

They drew attention to Parker's Gore, through their worldwide
     acclaim
Though the moose went north in January, we remember his
     fame
He brought a mystery to our hearts, and a message plain
The mighty forest, the wilderness, should ever so remain
Song on the wind, the wilderness
Song of the moose and the cow

Farmer's Alphabet

George Daniels was born in 1910 and grew up on a farm in Royalton. When he looks back now on farming as he knew it, he thinks it has changed a lot: "Farms back when I was a kid wasn't primarily dairy. Of course we had cattle, we had sheep, we had hogs, we cut logs, we sugared, we raised crops to sell; I mean it was just a farm. Today there's no farms left. They're all dairymen. I don't call a dairyman a farmer. They don't raise nothing except a field of corn and some hay. Go out and buy their vegetables and buy everything. They don't farm. Years ago milk and eggs was the wife's money. You done the milking, brought the milk in the house and she could make whatever she wanted, butter, cheese. But that was her income. But you didn't figure what you got out of your cows was income on the farm. You got your money out of logs, wood, bark, potatoes, chickens, pigs. There's always something you could scrape up for money. I think that people back then, I won't say they was more intelligent — maybe it was a case of necessity. But they was more self-sufficient. They knew what they wanted, they didn't ask somebody else to do it or hire somebody to do it. Everybody knew how to butcher a hog, take care of the meat, build a house, or raise a crop or alter a hog or anything else. You take a farm where there's been a couple lived on it and raised two or three kids, put them through graded school, and, if they was girls, some of them went to high school. But they ate, there was clothes, they learned life as it was then. They was capable of going out into the world and making their own families and not bother anybody. That way of life, of farming's gone."

This song, written by Margaret MacArthur, uses Mary Azarian's Farmer's Alphabet woodcuts as inspiration. Although in her book Mary prints "S is for stove," in her poster series she prints "S is for sow." In the latter case we sing "S is for sow, gives us pigs in the spring and T is for toad, catches bugs on the wing." The tune and pattern are from the traditional song, The Woodsman's Alphabet

Farmer's Alphabet

Traditional Dorian tune

A is for apple, you very well know, B is for barn, all covered with snow, C is for cow, milking now does begin, and D is for dog, sleeps when he comes in. And so merry are we, No mortal on earth is as happy as we, Sing I-der-ry, O-der-ry, I-der-ry dum, When the farm-er is well there is noth-ing goes wrong.

A is for apple, you very well know
B is for barn all covered with snow
C is for cow, milking now does begin, and
D is for dog, sleeps when he comes in

Chorus:
And so merry are, we
No mortal on earth is as happy as we
Sing Iderry, Oderry, I derry dum
When the farmer is well there is nothing goes wrong

E is for eggs we find in the hay
F is for farm on the hill far away
G is for garden to plant and to hoe, and
H is for horse that plows it just so

Chorus

I is for icicle, shiny and cold
J is for jump in the hay when we're bold
K is for kite that we fly in the wind, and
L is for lamb wool, to card and to spin

Chorus

M is for maple sugar in the spring
N is for neighbor who lends anything
O is for owl that hoots in the night, and
P is for pumpkin on Halloween night

Chorus

Q is for quilt with colors so bright
R is for rocker we sit in at night
S is for stove to cook and to heat, and
T is for toad, the bugs he does eat

Chorus

U is for underwear, keeps us so warm
V is for vegetables to store and to can
W is for winter for work and for play, and
X is for axe to chop wood all the day

Chorus

Y is for yawn, I'm ready for bed
Z is for zinnia all yellow and red
On this farm you can find many things, and
Now I've sung all I'm going to sing

Chorus

Index

Index

Audio Cassettes by Margaret MacArthur

Fifteen of the songs in this book as sung by Margaret MacArthur can be heard on the "Vermont Heritage Songbook Tape". *The Ballad of Devil's Hill* and *The Ballad of Runaway Pond* are found on Margaret's tape "Vermont Ballads and Broadsides" and she sings *Fifty Years Ago* on "Almanac of New England Farm Songs".

These audio cassettes are available from the Vermont Folklife Center.

Notes

Notes

Notes

DATE DUE

MAR 2 4 2002			
GAYLORD			PRINTED IN U.S.A